Introducing Structures

A TEXTBOOK FOR STUDENTS OF CIVIL AND
STRUCTURAL ENGINEERING, BUILDING AND
ARCHITECTURE

A. J. FRANCIS

Ph.D., M.Sc., M.C.E., F.I.C.E.,
F.I.Struct.E., F.I.E.Aust.

Emeritus Professor of Civil Engineering,
University of Melbourne, Victoria, Australia

PERGAMON PRESS

OXFORD · NEW YORK · TORONTO · SYDNEY · PARIS · FRANKFURT

U.K.	Pergamon Press Ltd., Headington Hill Hall, Oxford OX3 0BW, England
U.S.A.	Pergamon Press Inc., Maxwell House, Fairview Park, Elmsford, New York 10523, U.S.A.
CANADA	Pergamon of Canada, Suite 104, 150 Consumers Road, Willowdale, Ontario M2J 1P9, Canada
AUSTRALIA	Pergamon Press (Aust.) Pty. Ltd., P.O. Box 544, Potts Point, N.S.W. 2011, Australia
FRANCE	Pergamon Press SARL, 24 rue des Ecoles, 75240 Paris, Cedex 05, France
FEDERAL REPUBLIC OF GERMANY	Pergamon Press GmbH, 6242 Kronberg-Taunus, Hammerweg 6, Federal Republic of Germany

Copyright © 1980 A. J. Francis

First edition 1980

British Library Cataloguing in Publication Data
Francis, A J
Introducing Structures. - (Pergamon
international library).
1. Structural engineering
I. Title
624   TA633   79-41322

ISBN 0-08-022701-5 hardcover
ISBN 0-08-022702-3 flexicover

*Printed and bound in Great Britain by
William Clowes (Beccles) Limited, Beccles and London*

Contents

v

Preface

MOST structural textbooks deal with the *analysis* of particular types of structure (by far the greatest emphasis being given to plane rigid-jointed frames, which are only one of many types) and do not aim to give the student a grasp of how structures in general act as organisms to transmit and resist forces, or of the principles governing the *synthesis* or putting together of structures so as to be efficient in the use of material. The influence on the behaviour of the finished structure of the properties of the different structural materials which the engineer has at his disposal is not usually explained very well, either. And even in textbooks on structural *design*, the designer's task is not always clearly described in simple terms.

This book is an attempt to fill these gaps for the benefit of students of civil and structural engineering, building, and architecture. The main aim is to convey a *physical* understanding of the structural action of various kinds of structure (that is, how forces are transmitted through them and the stresses and deformations these forces produce) and how the engineer sets about the creative task of designing a structure for a particular function. The historical development of structural forms is touched on here and there in the discussion, and the main theme is also illustrated by reference to natural structures like plants, skeletons, and shells, and to structural failures and their causes. The presentation is almost entirely in non-mathematical terms, although an elementary knowledge of statics and structural mechanics is assumed.

The general approach of the book grew out of the author's experience as a teacher of the subject of engineering structures. Since the aim is a general one, to explain, in as brief a compass as possible, structural behaviour, form, and design, rather than to discuss comprehensively the various structural types, the reader will not expect to find every kind of trussed framework, for example, referred to and illustrated. Rather the book should be regarded as complementary to the more rigorous analytical and descriptive studies and the gradual initiation into the processes of creative design which the student normally undergoes.

The author is particularly indebted to Professor L. K. Stevens and Dr. D. S. Mansell, of Melbourne University, and also to one or two other friends, for reading and commenting on the draft manuscript, and to Miss Raugi Tamekus for her careful preparation of the typescript.

And finally he would like to thank his wife, without whose encouragement and support this book would probably never have been completed, and to whom it is dedicated.

CHAPTER 1

Introduction

ON 15 October 1970, at 11.50 a.m., a 112 m span of the Westgate bridge, under construction across the River Yarra in Melbourne, Australia, collapsed and fell into the river 40 m below. Thirty-five men working on the bridge were killed, completion was delayed by more than six years, and the cost of the acccident ran into many millions of dollars.

Disasters like this are mercifully rare. But when one does occur, the public is suddenly made aware of the heavy social responsibility carried by the structural engineer, and to some extent, possibly, the high degree of professional expertise required of him. Generally, however, structures are well behaved, and people take them and their creators very much for granted. Yet they play an all-pervading role in modern life, and account for a large proportion of the capital investment in the national infrastructure. For we live and work in houses, office blocks, and factories, relax in theatres or sports centres, and worship in churches and temples. When we travel we cross bridges, or board ship from a jetty or wharf. The water we drink has probably been stored in a reservoir impounded by a dam, and may have reached us along an aqueduct. Tall chimneys, power transmission pylons, cranes, television masts, cooling towers and so on are all part of the modern scene.

These are all building and civil engineering structures. A structure like the Eiffel Tower which overshadows Paris is so colossal that one wonders—especially if one stands on the top platform in a high wind—quite how safe it is, and how it was designed. Why should certain types of structure—suspension bridges, for example—have a characteristic and distinctive form? Why do modern structures look different from those in the past? How are they built, and what decides the choice of material used in them? Why, very occasionally, does one fail and make the headlines? This book is an attempt to introduce structures to the student of structural engineering, building, and architecture by answering such questions as these in simple terms.

Very broadly, a structure can be defined as something which forms a protective cover or casing for an object or living thing, or which carries weight, or supports or resists loads or forces of some kind. In this wide sense a snail's shell is a structure, and so is a man's skeleton, or the branches and trunk of a tree, or a spider's web. These are examples of natural structures, which have gradually evolved in the course of time to perform a particular function — and very efficiently they do so, as a rule. Taken in the broadest sense, man-made structures cover an extremely wide range of applications, including ships, aircraft, space vehicles, liquid and gas containers, car chassis, and even tables and chairs. In this book, however, we will be concerned mainly with the type of structure which is normally the responsibility of the structural engineer, working either on his own or in collaboration with an architect: these include buildings of all kinds, bridges, dams, jetties, deep-sea drilling platforms, masts, and so on. But we will be referring to other types of man-made structures as well as to natural structures in the course of the discussion, for the engineer can learn much about good design by studying the solutions achieved by the aircraft or ship designer, or by looking at the shape of shells or the skeletons of animals or plants.

Four main considerations or criteria govern nearly all structural design, and three of them were enunciated by Sir Henry Wooton, the Elizabethan poet, ambassador, and connoisseur, in his book *The Elements of Architecture.* Inspired by the writings of the Roman Vitruvius and the Renaissance architect Palladio, he gave as the requisites of good building *commodity, firmness,* and *delight* — or, as we would say in our less pungent modern phraseology, *suitability for its function; serviceability and safety;* and *good appearance* or *aesthetic satisfaction.* And today we would have to add a fourth criterion, *economy,* for though cost may have been no object to wealthy patrons of architecture like Sir Henry, it certainly is now.

By *commodity* or *function* we simply mean that since the structure was built for some purpose, it should be the aim of the designer to see that it performs its job well. This is so obviously desirable that it should go without saying. But in fact designers do not invariably keep it well in mind, and may be more preoccupied with the third criterion, *appearance*, than with making sure that their structure works well. We all know the handsome teapot that drips as it pours; and there are plenty of buildings and houses that are better to look at than to live and work in. On the other hand, some of the utilitarian structures designed by engineers, though they may function well, are ugly, because too little thought was given to what they would look like against their surroundings.

The second criterion of good building, *firmness,* is the special responsibility of the structural engineer. He must obviously make sure that his structure will not fall down. Further, it should not develop serious cracks or unsightly deflections, or vibrate alarmingly in the wind, or sink ignominiously into the ground. Good structural design calls for an understanding of the way in which structures sustain and transmit forces, and of the strength and other properties of structural materials. All structures deform under stress, and, unless they are built on rock, undergo some settlement. Cracking cannot be avoided in some materials. How much of this to allow, and how great a reserve of strength against failure there should be, inevitably affects the cost of the structure, and calls for engineering judgement.

The engineer was once defined, rather unkindly, as a man who can do for one dollar what any fool can do for two. While this definition hardly does justice to the special skills of the professional engineer, it does underline the importance of the last criterion, *economy*, in all engineering work. Nearly all structures are built with some limit of expenditure in mind, and this financial constraint has an important bearing on the influence of the other criteria. Cutting the cost can endanger the structure. If, on the other hand, it has been made unnecessarily strong it may not be competitive, and the designer must try to refine the details or perhaps alter the whole structural conception, with possibly a change in material which gives the required strength and stability more cheaply. In the end the structure may be cheaper even though it weighs more: for example, reinforced concrete framed buildings of moderate height usually work out cheaper than steel-framed ones, even though they are heavier. Weight can, however, be a prime consideration. An aircraft must be capable of getting off the ground under its own power, which sets entirely new and difficult constraints on the design; and if it is to operate economically the ratio of the payload to its own weight must be as high as possible. Not surprisingly, aircraft design is easily the most precise and refined in the whole field of structures, and it has had a great if sometimes belated influence on the design of the building and civil engineering structures with which we shall be mainly concerned in this book.

The true cost of a structure, of course, is not simply the cost of designing and building it, but this first cost plus the capitalized cost of maintaining it in good condition during its planned life. But designers — and clients — may not always care to face up to this, and prefer to opt instead for the choice that costs least to build, taking the biblical view that sufficient unto the day is the evil thereof. Cost is linked not only with firmness or safety but with the criterion of *delight* or *good appearance,* the visual impact which the structure makes on people. Canterbury Cathedral, regarded simply as a means of protecting worshippers from the weather, could have been built much more cheaply; but then it would probably not have had an atmosphere appropriate to worship, or such power to awe and entrance the beholder. The larger the structure, the more difficult it becomes to give it a particular appearance independent of structural requirements; in fact, one of the remarkable features of Gothic churches is the success with which the demands both of aesthetics and strength were met in unprecedentedly large buildings made of such a difficult and limited material as stone, at a time when structural science was non-existent. In the greatest of all structures, suspension bridges, the general form is always the same, because the hanging cable is the only possible structural shape for very large spans. It is just as well that the shape of a hanging cable is generally thought to be pleasing.

The materials used in structures have always had a strong influence on their form and appearance. Each structural material, especially if it is a natural product like stone or timber, has peculiarities and limitations which determine structural form to an extent not often realized by the layman. We start our study of structures, therefore, by looking at the principal characteristics of building materials which have a bearing on strength and stability, in particular the properties of stone, brick, concrete, timber, iron, and steel.

We then introduce the reader to the simpler kinds of structural types — cables and arches, trusses and beams — before considering how structures in general collapse and how their strength can be calculated. The flow of stress through material of various shapes, and how different stress conditions affect strength, are then discussed, and there is an introduction to the important and complicated question of flexural instability or buckling, which has caused so many structural failures. We then look at some more recent structural developments such as prestressing, shell and cable structures, and the frameworks of modern buildings.

Structural engineering is a technical skill which, like extractive metallurgy, was well developed as a practical art long before the underlying sciences were understood. Although the theory of structures is only about two centuries old, very remarkable structural feats had been achieved at least as long ago as 3000 B.C. Building, in fact, is one of the traditional crafts, in which practice at any time is strongly influenced by that of the past — sometimes the distant past. In an amusing poem of Kipling's, one of the Pharaohs suddenly appears on a modern building site — and finds everything very familiar! Within living memory, at least, there was much more than a grain of truth in this; methods of making bricks and building in brick, for example, had until recently hardly changed for many hundreds of years. In a study of structures their historical development is instructive as well as interesting, and throughout the discussion we will try to convey something of this — how man has made use of whatever materials were to hand, and developed new ones with better properties; how he has taken risks in design and construction in the absence of theory to guide him, and learned painfully from his mistakes; and how, gradually, he has evolved new structural systems to meet fresh and more exacting requirements.

The structural designer's art is a highly skilled and difficult one. He must, as we have said, possess a grasp of structural action — how loads and forces are supported by and transmitted through structures, what stresses and deformations are set up, and how failure in one of its many manifestations finally occurs. But the designer is not merely an analyst: he is first and foremost a creator of structures. In Chapter 11 we try to convey an idea of the process of design, of the forces on structures, how the designer assembles his structure in imagination, how he ensures its safety, the assumptions he is obliged to make, and the uncertainties in the final solution.

At one time, advances in structural form or size could only proceed by trial and error, and inevitably there were many failures. To a much smaller extent this is still true, in spite of the great increase in our knowledge of structural behaviour in the last 200 years. Engineers, too, are only human. They occasionally omit to take account of existing knowledge either in their own field or a related one; or to make sure that communications are good, that everyone concerned with the creation and realization of the structure understands what is intended and has a clear role to play; or to visualize how it might behave in unusual circumstances; or even to do their sums properly. Nowadays, fortunately, major structural failures are well documented and their causes identified for the benefit of the profession. The last chapter contains an account of some of these and what has been learned from them.

CHAPTER 2

Structural Materials

To UNDERSTAND why structures have developed as they have in the course of history, and behave as they do, we must know something of the characteristics of structural materials. First we must be clear what we mean by a structural material. It is the material—steel, concrete, or stone, for instance—which is used to make those parts of the structure which carry the load and give it strength and stability. For instance, in a steel-framed office building the steel is the structural material. Such a structure contains other materials, those used to clothe or clad it to protect it from the weather, or in the internal linings and partitions. The "cladding" of a building can, in fact, strengthen it considerably— anyone who has erected an aluminium-alloy framed greenhouse knows that the glass stiffens the structure and gives it added strength—but it is not primarily the structural material.

Strength is the most important property of a structural material, since it is strength which determines the force which the weakest part of a structure can carry before the material at that point fails, and the structure as a whole may collapse. The strength (or more precisely the *ultimate strength*) of a material is the stress (defined as load per unit area of cross-section) at which failure takes place, and is usually measured by testing a specimen of the material in a testing machine.

The material in a structure may fail either in tension or in compression. Accordingly, the designer needs to know both the tensile and the compressive ultimate strength of his material. These are determined by pulling a specimen apart or squeezing it together. In the latter case it has to be short and squat in shape: a slender rod will buckle at a much lower load which does not give a measure of the compressive strength.

Table 1 gives typical values of ultimate strengths for the most common structural materials.* They fall into two groups. Those labelled "traditional" have been used by builders and engineers since the earliest times. Two of them, stone and timber, occur naturally. The other two are man-made. Sun-dried bricks of clay were in use in the Tigris-Euphrates valleys of Iraq as early as 4500 B.C., and by 3000 B.C. the art of baking or "firing" bricks to vitrify them and give them much greater strength had been discovered. A weak concrete consisting of lime mixed with stone and sand was also in use in the early civilizations of the Middle East, and the Romans invented "hydraulic" cement, in which the addition of silicates to the lime produces a much stronger concrete. Modern concrete made from Portland cement, which is stronger still, dates from the first half of the nineteenth century.

All these early structural materials, except timber, had two particular characteristics. By the standards of modern materials they were rather weak; and they were all much weaker in tension than in compression. Stone and brick structures, furthermore, were built up from individual units with, usually, a weak lime mortar in the joints. Thus the tensile strength of the assembled structure was only as great as that of the adhesion between the units, and this was very small indeed. In fact, in most important Roman structures in stone no mortar at all was used—the Pont du Gard in southern France is a typical example. So in these early structures no tension could be permitted, and this greatly restricted the range of structural forms which were possible, and their size.

Stone, brick, concrete, and cast iron (the first of the modern structural materials) are all *brittle* materials, which under normal conditions of use are not only much weaker in tension than in compression (between one-fifth and one-tenth as strong) but have a tendency to fail abruptly by cracking or splintering. Except for stone like granite, they are also much weaker even in compression than wrought iron and steel, as Table 1 shows. The latter are equally strong in tension and compression (actually, the compressive strength of a short specimen of steel or iron is somewhat indeterminate since it merely goes on squashing once it

---

*Nowadays weight, force, strength, and other quantities are expressed in International Units. The unit of force is the newton, which is equal to 0.225 pounds weight. Stress, which was traditionally expressed in pounds per square inch in English-speaking countries, is now described in newtons per square millimetre. One newton per square mm (1 N/mm^2) = 145.04 pounds per square inch.

TABLE 1: Typical Properties of Structural Materials

(1) Material			(2) Ultimate strength σ_u (N/mm²)		(3) Specific strength S (metres)		(4) Modulus of elasticity E (N/mm²)	(5) Specific modulus M (metres × 10³)	(6) Conventional description of material
			Tensile	Compressive	Tensile	Compressive			
Traditional	Stone	Granite	40	200	1400	7000	45,000	1.57	Brittle
		Limestone (Portland stone)	5	40	225	1800	30,000	1.35	Brittle
		Brick (medium strength)	6	60	320	3200	30,000	1.60	
	Timber (spruce)	Along grain	120	30	24,000	6000	15,000	3.00	See text
		Across grain	3.5	—	700	—	—	—	
Modern	Portland cement concrete	For mass and normal reinforced work	2	20	90	900	25,000	1.12	Brittle
		For High-strength prestressed work	6	60	270	2700	40,000	1.80	
	Iron and steel	Cast iron	200	800	2900	11,600	120,000	1.73	
		Wrought iron	300	> 300	4000	> 4000	190,000	2.53	Ductile
		Mild or structural steel	450	> 450	6000	> 6000	210,000	2.80	
		Medium high-strength steel	600	> 600	8000	> 8000	210,000	2.80	
		High-strength prestressing wire	2000	—	26,700	—	210,000	2.80	
		Aluminium alloy (Dural)	450	> 450	17,000	> 17,000	70,000	2.80	

becomes plastic). Furthermore, they do not normally behave in a brittle way under stress, but are *ductile,* extending a great deal before tensile failure, and not shattering under compression or impact. A familiar illustration of the contrast between brittle and ductile materials is the behaviour of blackboard chalk and a piece of steel wire formed by straightening a paperclip. When bent the one snaps abruptly; the other bends but does not break.

In small quantities, steel and wrought iron have been produced by blacksmiths for thousands of years, the former for armour, weapons, and cutting blades, the latter for bolts, rods, nails, and chain. At the beginning of the nineteenth century a vital new step was taken. It was discovered how to mass-produce wrought iron in large pieces, in the form of plates and bars which could be riveted together into structural members such as beams and the ties and struts of trusses. Even before 1850, Robert Stephenson had built wrought-iron beams of box section with a span of no less than 140 m for the Britannia railway bridge over the Menai Straits in North Wales. A little later mild steel was produced in large quantities. Entirely new structural possibilities were thus opened up, both in the size and span of structures and in the diversity of forms that were now possible.

The earliest form in which iron was used in modern construction was, in fact, the brittle cast iron. Mass production of large castings became possible towards the end of the eighteenth century in England, and cast iron had a brief popularity in structures where it was mainly in compression, in arched bridges and in columns in factory and mill buildings. When it was tried in beams and girders for railway bridges, where it was partly in tension, however, it was a failure and was quickly superseded by wrought iron and then steel. Its most spectacular success was in the framework of the Crystal Palace built for the Exhibition of 1851 in London.

Timber is to some extent in a place of its own. It has substantial tensile strength along the grain but is much weaker in compression and across the grain, and this makes it difficult to connect pieces under tension—at least, this was so until modern timber connections were invented.

All structures have weight, and their own weight is one of the loads that they have to carry. The larger a structure of a given type, the more important its own weight becomes in relation to other loads, until a size is reached at which it can only just support its own weight. Galileo first realized this, and we can demonstrate it by a simple example, that of a bar of uniform cross-section hanging freely under its own weight. How long can it be before it breaks off at the top?

To find this, we simply put the weight of the bar equal to its tensile strength. Then, using the symbols shown in Fig. 2.1, we have

Weight = volume × density = $AL\rho g$
(where g is the acceleration due to gravity)
and
Tensile strength = $A \times \sigma_u$

where σ_u is the ultimate tensile strength of the material.
Equating these, we have

$$AL\rho g = A\sigma_u$$

from which

$$L = \frac{\sigma_u}{\rho g} = S, \text{ where } S \text{ is called the specific strength.}$$

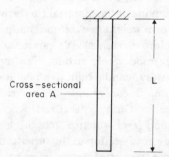

Cross-sectional area A

L

FIG. 2.1. Bar of uniform cross-section hanging under its own weight.

There is thus an absolute limit S to the length which the bar can attain which is independent of the cross-sectional area (as we should expect, for if we double the area we also double the weight to be carried, and gain nothing thereby).

As the size of a bar of any given shape increases, its strength goes up in proportion to the square of the ruling dimension, but the weight increases as the cube. Sooner or later, therefore, weight must overtake strength. We have shown this to be true for the simplest case of stressing, direct stress; but it also applies in bending and in more complex stress situations. For every kind of structure, in fact, there is a maximum possible size beyond which it cannot carry even its own weight. In his *Two New Sciences,* published in 1638, Galileo pointed out that it is impossible to construct ships, palaces, or temples of enormous size, and that in Nature there is a limit to the size of trees and animals of a certain kind; and, further, that the larger any structure becomes which is subject to its own weight, the stockier and more bulky it gets. Thus, very large bridges are heavier in proportion to small ones of the same type; and the bones of very large animals, like elephants, are much stockier and thicker than those of small ones like mice, and account for a much larger percentage of their total weight. On the other hand, in aquatic animals, where the weight is almost completely supported by the buoyancy of the water, the skeletal proportions vary very little between a small porpoise and the largest whale.

Table 1 gives in metres, in round figures, the specific strengths of the materials listed. For the traditional brittle materials the value in compression is of main interest, for it is the height to which a column of uniform cross-section made of the material can be built before it crushes at the base under its own weight (we assume that it is stocky enough not to buckle sideways before it crushes). We can see at a glance that even a material that is only moderately strong, like the concrete used for general construction work, can be built to a height of about 900 m—far higher than any column in concrete, stone, or brickwork has ever been raised. Even in the tallest Gothic cathedrals, where the cross-sectional area of stone at ground level which is actually load-bearing is only a fraction of the average cross-section of the superimposed masonry, there is no danger of collapse from crushing of the stone at the base, if it has a reasonably high compressive strength.

Stone, brick, and concrete compare quite well with steel in compression, and of course they are never used in tension. What is really interesting is the excellent performance of timber. In compression the *S* value for a typical sample of spruce is as high as that of mild steel, and in tension it is four times as good. Indeed, the essential wood substance of the cells, which gives the spruce its strength, accounts for only about one-third of the cross-section (the rest is mainly water and air) so that the specific strength of the wood fibre itself is about 12,000 m in compression and 48,000 m in tension. These would, in fact, be the values if the timber could be compressed laterally so as to eliminate all the water and air and form a much denser material. They are far in excess of those for any man-made material, and are a remarkable illustration of the economy and efficiency of the structural arrangements achieved in Nature. The aluminium alloys, also, have high specific strengths because of their lightness compared with their strength. This explains why wood was so extensively used in early aircraft, and why aluminium alloys still are. Aircraft are structures which not only carry loads but must be capable of being raised into the air under their own power. The structural materials used in them must therefore have as high a value of *S* as possible. Only very recently, in supersonic aircraft, the skins of which become very hot in flight, have designers been obliged to turn to high-strength steels and titanium alloys for strength at high temperatures.

A much fuller picture of the relative performance of different structural materials than can be gained from Table 1 is presented by the comparative stress-strain curves obtained from tests on specimens (Fig. 2.2). Not only does this demonstrate the great superiority of the modern steels in strength, but it also reveals another most important property, their ductility. A standard test specimen of mild steel, for example, extends by more than 20 per cent over the gauge length before it breaks, whereas a specimen of normal concrete has a breaking strain in tension of only about 0.01 per cent. Even in compression the strain at failure is only of the order of 0.15 per cent. The graph demonstrates much more vividly than a mere statement the difference between brittle and ductile behaviour.

Another fact of great importance emerges from an examination of the figure. All the curves have an initial straight or nearly straight portion within which, if the test specimen is unloaded, it will recover its initial shape and length. If loaded beyond this *elastic* range and unloaded, the specimen is left with a permanent extension or set. It is clearly undesirable for a structure to suffer obvious permanent distortion after it is first loaded, and ever since it first became possible to calculate stresses with some degree of precision—for the last 150 years or so—it has been a prime aim in structural design to ensure that the maximum

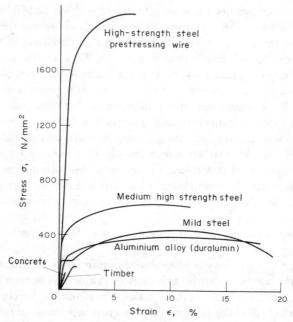

FIG. 2.2. Stress-strain relationships for various structural materials.

calculated stress in the structure due to the loads it is expected to carry in service (the *working* or *design* loads) remains well within this elastic region. Usually the working stress is one-half to two-thirds of the elastic limit. (Because of the great difficulty of calculating precisely the stress at points where there is a discontinuity or change of section, *local* stresses can be much higher than the calculated value and even well above the elastic limit under normal loading, but these need not endanger the structure if the material is sufficiently ductile: the aim is to make sure that high stresses do occur only locally.) The ratio

$$\frac{\text{ultimate strength}}{\text{design stress}}$$

is usually known as the *stress factor of safety*.

During its normal life, therefore, the structure responds to loads and other forces in a manner dictated largely by the small part of the stress-strain curve of the material which lies within the elastic limit. For the strong ductile materials, steel and the aluminium alloys, this elastic range is linear, and the slope of the stress-strain line (i.e. the ratio

$$\frac{\text{stress}}{\text{strain}} = \frac{\sigma}{\varepsilon} = E)$$

is known as the modulus of elasticity of the material. For brittle materials like stone and concrete, the elastic range is not quite straight but is close enough to it for normal design purposes.

Column 4 of Table 1 gives the E values of the materials listed, and it can be seen that E is much greater for the steels than for the brittle materials and for timber. It is also three times as great as for the aluminium alloys. Now the working stresses in mild steel and the alloy listed are roughly the same, since their ultimate strengths are similar. If, therefore, two bridges of the same span and type were designed in these two materials to carry the same loads, the members would be about the same in cross-section. If the same vehicle passed over each bridge, the alloy bridge would deflect about three times as much as the steel one. Excessive flexibility is undesirable in structures, one reason being that people dislike noticeable vibration and deflection in bridges and buildings. The high E value of steel is one of its greatest advantages over the aluminium alloys. Such a direct comparison cannot be made between steel and the brittle materials or timber, however, because the working stresses in the latter are much lower and members are in consequence heavier.

In cases where the weight of the structure forms a large part of the total load, as it does in very large structures or in aircraft, one *can* make a more meaningful comparison of the elastic efficiency of different materials. To return to the bar of Fig. 2.1, the average stress σ in the bar is half the stress at the top, i.e.

$$\sigma = \frac{AL\rho g}{2A} = \frac{L\rho g}{2}$$

The extension δ of the bar under its own weight, therefore, if it remains elastic, is

$$\delta = \frac{\sigma L}{E} = \frac{L^2 \rho g}{2E} = \frac{L^2}{2M}$$

where $M = E/\rho g$ is defined as the specific modulus of the material. Just as

S is a measure of the *strength* of a material in a structure which carries only its own weight, so M is a measure of its *stiffness*. The higher the value of M, the less the bar will extend under its own weight. As column 5 of Table 1 shows, steel is better than the brittle materials, but only about as good as the aluminium alloy, because although the latter stretches three times as much under the same stress, it is only one-third as dense. The really surprising material, again, is timber, which is better than either. In fact, the cellulose fibre which forms the cell structure of wood has a specific modulus of no less than 8500 m, far higher than that of any man-made structural material. This is another reason why wood has been used so much in aircraft construction.

The above expression for δ leads us to another conclusion of great significance in relation to the *scale* of structures. Given two similar bars of different size, it will be seen that their extensions under their own weight are proportional not to the scale but to the *square* of the scale. Thus, if a matchstick 50 mm long and a beam of the same material and the same proportions but 100 times as big, or 5 m long, hang freely, the beam will extend not 100 times as much as the matchstick but 100^2 or 10,000 times as much. The same rule applies to the central deflection if the matchstick and the beam are supported at the ends, or in fact in any other way. Thus a limit is set by its own weight to the size to which a structure of a given form can be built, not only by excessive stress, as we saw earlier, but also by excessive deflection in relation to its dimensions.

As we have seen, there are two main points of difference between the properties of the brittle and the ductile materials used in structures which are brought out in Fig. 2.2 and Table 1. They are:

(1) The brittle materials are much weaker in tension than in compression, whereas the ductile materials have roughly equal tensile and compressive ultimate strengths;

(2) The brittle materials fail after a very small strain, even in compression, and after stress-strain behaviour which is not very non-linear, whereas the ductile materials, after the limit of elastic behaviour is reached at, very roughly, half the ultimate strength, can undergo a considerably greater non-elastic strain before failure.

This second point of difference further weakens a structure of brittle material under tension. To illustrate, let us look at a very simple structure consisting of three vertical bars 1, 2, and 3, all of the same material and cross-sectional area A, and pinned to a rigid horizontal beam and to a ceiling as shown (Fig. 2.3a). Bar 1 is half as long as the other two bars. Let us suppose first that the material of the bars is brittle, with the linear tensile stress-strain relationship shown at (b). The ultimate load capacity of each bar is evidently equal to $A\sigma_u$.

Because of the symmetry of the structure and of the loading, when a load W is hung from the rigid beam at A each bar extends by the same amount δ. Since bar 1 is only half as long as the others, the strain and therefore the stress and force in it will be twice as great as in the outer bars. If W is gradually increased in magnitude, therefore, the force in the middle bar will finally reach its ultimate load capacity $F = A\sigma_u$, and it will fail abruptly. At this point, as we can see from Fig. 2.3d,

$$W = F + \frac{F}{2} + \frac{F}{2} = 2F.$$

The failure of bar 1 leaves bars 2 and 3 to carry the load W, which they can only just do. They are also at the point of failure, so that the ultimate load capacity W_u of the structure has been reached. The plot of W against δ, seen at (e), is linear right up to the point of failure.

Now let us see what happens if the material of the bars is *ductile*, with the same ultimate tensile strength σ_u as before but with the idealized stress-strain graph shown at (f), in which there is a purely plastic region 1-2. (The graph is somewhat similar to the first part of the graph for mild steel shown in Fig. 2.2.) As W is increased, the stress in bar 1 reaches σ_u as before, when the load W equals $2F$. But instead of breaking, the bar starts extending at constant stress, the material being in the region 1-2. W can be increased further, and the additional load is carried by the bars 2 and 3 until the stress in them also reaches the ultimate stress σ_u. At this point no more load can be applied: all three bars go on extending at constant stress until the material in the middle bar reaches point 2 on the stress-strain graph. Here its ductility is exhausted and it breaks, and immediately the other two bars fail also. At failure in this case, all three bars carry the maximum possible load (see (g)) from which W_u is obviously equal to $3F$. The plot of W against the downward movement of the beam is now as shown at (h).

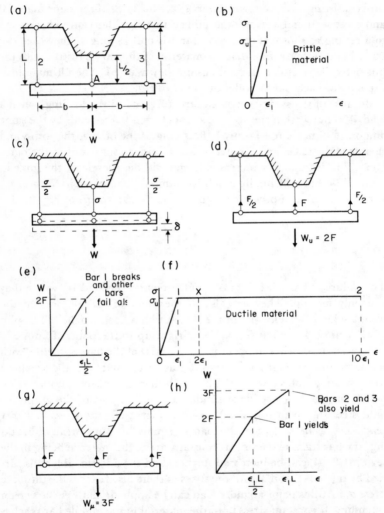

FIG. 2.3. Behaviour of a structure with three bars of (i) brittle, (ii) ductile material.

What has happened here is of great significance. The strength of the *material* and of the individual *members* is the same in the two cases, but the strength of the *structure* made of ductile material is 50 per cent greater than that of the one with brittle material. This is due entirely to the ductility of the material beyond the elastic limit, which enables the stress in all the members to reach the ultimate tensile strength before the structure fails. Since in the vast majority of cases the stress is not uniform throughout the structure in the elastic range of behaviour, this capacity for redistribution of stress after the elastic limit is passed anywhere is an extremely important consequence of ductility. Furthermore, signs of distress — obvious distortion, or yield of the material — can often be detected well before failure as the most highly stressed parts deform plastically, and such advance warning of the onset of failure is valuable.

There is, of course, a limit to the extent to which the process of redistribution of stress can go, and this depends on the available ductility of the material and the type of structure. In our example it was completely achieved, and the material in the middle bar was still only at point X on the graph (f) at failure. But in more complicated structures with less ductile material, complete redistribution of stress might not be possible.

The process we have been discussing takes place not only in complete structures but — and this is just as important in relation to the strength of structures — in the various parts of them. For instance, consider a wide plate (Fig. 2.4), forming part of a member in a truss, which is subjected to a tensile stress σ. If a very small hole is made in the middle of the plate, then so long as the whole of the material remains elastic the stress at either side of the hole rises to approximately 3σ. If the plate is made of brittle material it will fail from cracking at the hole as soon as the stress there reaches the ultimate value σ_u, while the bulk of the cross-section at the hole carries a stress only one-third of this. If, however, the material is ductile, with a sufficiently large plastic region, redistribution of stress will take place after the elastic limit has been passed at the hole, and the entire cross-section will be stressed up to the ultimate strength σ_u before failure. The plate will thus be approximately three times as strong as it would be if the material were brittle. Since in most of the steel structures now in service the members are connected by riveting or bolting, which require holes to be made in the material, ductility is an essential characteristic of structural steel.

In certain types of structure this process of adjustment of internal

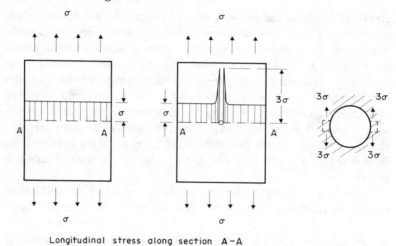

Longitudinal stress along section A–A

(i) Plain plate   (ii) Plate with very small
                                central hole

FIG. 2.4. Stress distribution in a very wide plate with a small circular hole.

stress cannot occur no matter how ductile the material is. For example, in the two-bar frame of Fig. 2.5 the force in each bar is always 0.5 W,

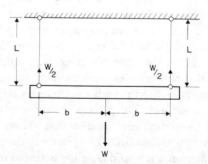

FIG. 2.5. Forces in a two-bar structure.

whatever the cross-section of each or the elastic properties of the material. No redistribution of force between the two members is possible as the material yields, and when one of the bars fails the structure collapses. Such a structure is called *statically determinate*, because the internal forces are determined by statics, without regard to the sizes or elastic properties of the various parts. The three-bar structure of Fig. 2.3, on the other hand, is *statically indeterminate*: the internal forces depend on the relative cross-sectional areas of the members and on the elastic characteristics of the material, as well as on the laws of statics.

It may appear from what has been said that there is always a clear distinction between brittle and ductile materials, but this is not so. Certainly stone, concrete, cast iron, and brick are normally brittle, and steel is normally ductile. But we know from looking at rock strata exposed in a cliff face or a quarry that under conditions of intense heat and high pressure such as have occurred inside the earth's crust, and given enough time, rock can flow and be distorted in a ductile manner. The effect of pressure alone is enough to change completely the behaviour of a specimen of rock or concrete in compression. Figure 2.6 shows this very vividly for specimens of marble which were subjected to

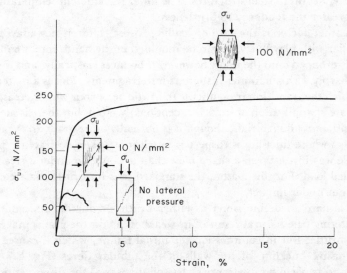

FIG. 2.6. Behaviour of marble specimens under longitudinal compression combined with lateral compression.

hydrostatic pressure in an oil-filled vessel and then, in addition, compressed at the ends in the normal way. Without lateral pressure the failure was brittle with very little compressive strain. At a hydrostatic pressure of 100 N/mm^2 (= 1000 atmospheres) the compressive strength was five times as great, and the behaviour as ductile as that of a specimen of mild steel. If the tests had been conducted at, say, 300°C instead of at normal temperature, the rock would have been even more ductile.

Conversely, if a specimen of mild steel is subjected to hydrostatic *tension* and then tested in direct tension in a testing machine, it will behave in a less ductile way than usual, and if the hydrostatic tensile stress is great enough it will be quite brittle, with virtually no plastic extension before failure. Even if tested in compression there will be a tendency to brittleness. Such conditions of hydrostatic tension (triaxial tensile stress) can easily occur in a tension member in which there are abrupt changes in shape or discontinuities. In a thick plate with a hole in it, for example, there is triaxial tension in the interior near the sides of the hole when the plate is put into tension, and it is almost unavoidable around welding details in steel structures. The lower the ambient temperature, the greater the tendency to brittleness.

Another factor is the rate of loading. Most children nowadays are familiar with play putty. It can be moulded in the hands into a ball; if this is dropped onto the floor, however, it bounces elastically; and if it is hit sharply with a hammer it shatters into fragments. This is a material in which the transition from ductile to brittle behaviour with increase in the rate of application of stress is exceptionally rapid, but there is such a transition in all materials, though it is normally more gradual. A piece of steel whose ductility is suspect is much more likely to fracture in a brittle way if it is given a sharp blow than it would be under a steadily applied load. For this reason, the standard tests for brittleness are carried out under impact.

It is hard to define wood as either brittle or ductile. Its habit of splintering (the natural result of its weakness across the grain) makes it look brittle. But in compression the initial failure, which is caused by progressive buckling of the walls of the tubular fibres (Fig. 2.7), is followed by yielding in a more or less plastic way as the fibres continue to deform along the inclined line of failure. Timber is normally used in

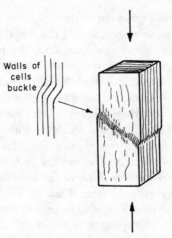

Walls of
cells
buckle

FIG. 2.7. Behaviour of timber specimen under longitudinal compression.

bending, and this progressive crushing on the compressive side of a beam transfers load to the tension side, on the same general principle that we have seen at work in the two examples already discussed. A timber beam may thus be up to twice as strong as would be calculated simply on an elastic distribution of stress and on the compressive strength of the wood. This gradual transfer of stress is accompanied by creaking and groaning which gives ample warning of the approach of complete failure. Coal miners objected strongly when steel props were first introduced in mines because they were used to the warning noises made by timber props. Larch props, which emit a loud warning crack some time before failure, are still widely used in U.K. mines for this reason.

One undesirable feature of timber is its tendency to creep under stress. After a year the deflection of a beam of green timber can be three to six times the deflection immediately the load is applied, and the results of long-term creep appear in old church roofs. Concrete also creeps appreciably, though less than timber, and this must be allowed for especially in the design of prestressed concrete structures. In the Gladesville bridge (Fig. 3.18) in Sydney, Australia, for example, the effective long-term modulus of elasticity of the concrete in the arch ribs after shrinkage (due to drying out of the concrete) and creep under the compressive stress was only one-third of the initial modulus.

We have seen that, apart from ductility, the two most important characteristics of structural materials are *strength* and *stiffness*, as measured by the value of E, the modulus of elasticity. It is now known that E is related to the attractive force between adjacent atoms in solid materials. For atoms of a given element—iron, for example—this force has a definite value, and E can be calculated with a high degree of accuracy from this knowledge. Since iron accounts for all but one per cent or so of the content of the structural steels, E hardly varies from steel to steel, and there is no possibility of increasing its value by heat treatment or by mechanically working the steel. Thus one of the drawbacks of the aluminium alloys, their low stiffness, is unavoidable.

On the other hand, the *strength* of structural materials—steels and concrete and bricks in particular—has been continually rising over the past century with advances in manufacturing technology. Even so, there is still much scope for improvement. The theoretical tensile strength of iron, for example, like its modulus of elasticity, can be calculated from the interatomic forces, and is found to be about $E/6$, or about 35,000 N/mm^2, which is more than seventeen times that of the strongest structural steel, high-strength prestressing wire. Flaws in the interatomic structure, and (especially in brittle material) fine cracks, account for the much lower strength of commercially produced steels. It has recently become possible by new manufacturing techniques to make fine fibres or "whiskers" of elements like iron and carbon with very few flaws, and these have strengths approaching the theoretical values. Gas turbine blades, for example, have been made with such materials. But whether it will ever be feasible to do this with structural materials, which are required in bulk, is an open question. In concrete another approach has recently proved very successful. Short lengths (50 mm or so) of fine steel wire added to the mix make concrete much stronger in tension and more resistant to shrinkage cracking and to impact, and this technique is now becoming popular.

A particularly valuable property of steel is that it is more or less *isotropic*: that is, its strength and elastic properties are almost the same in whatever direction it is stressed. This is not quite true even for mild steel, which has slightly better mechanical properties in the direction of rolling than at right angles to it; and the very high strength of prestressing wire results partly from the fact that the crystalline structure of the steel is modified to some extent by the cold-working of the wire-drawing process and aligned along the axis of the wire. Wood, however, is an example of an anisotropic material. In nature it is only stressed along the grain, i.e. in the direction of the wood cells (in fact, the growth of the cells is stimulated by the presence of stress, and is encouraged to take place in the direction of stress), and is extremely weak at right angles to the grain. When used for structural purposes, it is impossible to avoid stressing the wood to some extent across the grain, and this creates difficulties, especially in connections.

However good the strength and stiffness of a structural material, it is not of much use unless it can be formed into shapes which meet the functional requirements of the structure and are structurally economical. For example, even if stone were equally strong in tension and compression, it would be quite impracticable to shape a piece of it into a structure like the helical reinforced concrete ramp in the Penguin Pool at the London Zoo (Fig. 2.8). Cubical, cylindrical, or rectangular

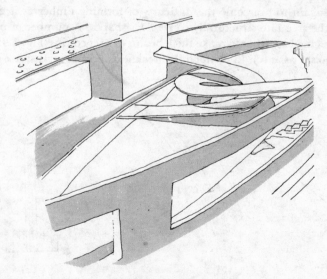

FIG. 2.8. Penguin Pool, London Zoo.

blocks are the only feasible units in stone. The lack of tensile strength between units, whether jointed dry or with mortar, virtually restricted stone construction in the ancient world to columns, arches, and domes, all of which act in compression, and to the relatively short, deep lintel beams which are a feature of Egyptian and Greek building.

The first structural material capable of being formed into a variety of shapes was concrete, and the Romans used it in some of their domed roofs. But the extreme versatility with which it is now employed in curved beams, plates, thin shells of almost every conceivable shape, and even for the hulls of small boats, only became possible with the introduction of steel reinforcement embedded in the concrete to carry the tensile stresses. The formwork required to make complicated shapes can, however, be expensive, and another, much more recent development has followed the invention of very strong epoxy resin glues, which have a tensile strength equal to the compressive strength of the highest quality concrete. Plates of reinforced or prestressed concrete may be glued together to make joists or other types of member, and steel strips can be glued to the underside of slabs or beams to strengthen them.

Gluing has been common practice in wood construction for many years, again to overcome the difficulty of forming timber as it comes from the tree into structurally convenient shapes. A number of planks can be glued together to make thick beams or arched ribs (Fig. 2.9a and b) or joists, as at (c). In plywood the weakness of timber transverse to the

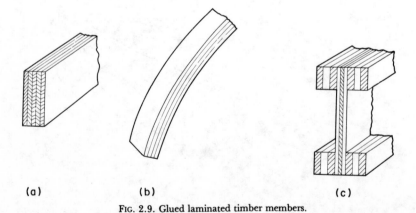

(a)   (b)   (c)

FIG. 2.9. Glued laminated timber members.

orientation of the grain is overcome by gluing together three or more thin sheets peeled off a trunk by a long knife blade. Individual sheets have virtually no strength at right angles to the direction of the wood cells, but the grain is varied in direction in successive sheets so that the finished product is equally strong in all directions.

Hardboard and other particle boards are made from wood scrap which is fragmented and then bonded together into sheets with a resin. These reconstituted products are noticeably weaker and more flexible than wood or plywood of the same cross-section, because of the shortness of the individual fragments of fibre and their random orientation in the particle board. These developments have, however, meant that wood is now used in ways which were not possible before—in large thin sheets in panelling and lining in building construction, for the inner surface of concrete formwork where a smooth finish is needed, in furniture, in the webs of built-up timber girders, and so on.

Next to concrete, steel is easily the most "formable" of the structural materials. It can be rolled in joist form up to a metre deep, and in a variety of other shapes (Fig. 2.10a to d). Plates and sections can be bent

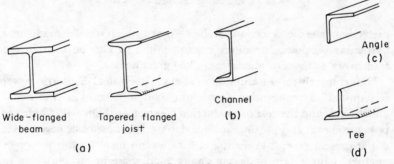

Wide-flanged beam

Tapered flanged joist

(a)

Channel
(b)

Angle
(c)

Tee
(d)

FIG. 2.10. Structural steel sections.

and shaped cold or with a little heat. The invention of electric arc welding has enabled almost any shape of built-up member to be made from plates and sections. Before the days of welding, however, riveting together of flat or bent plates and sections produced such huge structures as the Forth railway bridge. There is no doubt that the ability of steel to be shaped and joined has led as much as any other property to its pre-eminence as a structural material.

So strong was the tradition of steel construction, in fact, that when the aluminium alloys came onto the structural market after 1945 the first joist sections which were produced had precisely the same shape as the tapered-flanged sections then in use in steel. The taper was necessary at that time in steel production because of the difficulty of rolling parallel-sided flanges (this problem has since been solved). What was completely ignored was the fact that aluminium alloy sections are not rolled but extruded, by forcing the hot metal through a die cut to the required profile, like toothpaste out of a tube. Quite different types of section, and much more intricate ones, can be produced than are possible by rolling (Fig. 2.11). Provided the quantity needed justifies the

FIG. 2.11. Extruded aluminium alloy sections.

high cost of the die, a section can be designed which is tailor-made for a particular purpose. Ingenious examples of this can be seen in the framework of modern aluminium-alloy greenhouses.

Unfortunately for the aluminium alloys, a great deal of electric power is required to reduce the aluminium oxide (bauxite) to the metal aluminium, and the cost of production is extremely high even where the power is cheap. It is the one structural material whose basic cost rules it out at present except, in the main, for uses in which, for one reason or another, light-weight or exceptionally good resistance to corrosion (a characteristic of these alloys) is desirable.

CHAPTER 3

Structural Action: Cables and Arches

Introduction

In the last chapter we discussed the more important properties of structural materials as they affect the behaviour of structures subjected to loads and other forces. The structural engineer must also have an understanding of structural action—of the way, in other words, in which forces pass through a structure of a given type and configuration; and how, if the forces are great enough, excessive deflections and cracking make the structure unserviceable, or it collapses.

It must be said at the outset that this is an elusive subject. The great majority of structural textbooks deal with the analysis of the forces, stresses, and deformations in structures of various kinds under load. The science of structural action, and the concomitant art of creating structures (a *synthetical* as opposed to an *analytical* thought process) are topics much less commonly discussed in the literature.

Statically Determinate and Statically Indeterminate Structures

In Chapter 2 we drew a distinction between statically determinate and statically indeterminate structures. A very simple example of a statically determinate structure was discussed, the two-bar frame shown in Fig. 2.5. It was pointed out that when this frame is loaded as shown, the forces in the members are found simply by applying the laws of statics. This means that the bar forces are independent of the relative cross-sectional areas of the bars and the elastic properties of the material used to make them, and are solely a function of the geometrical configuration of the structure and the nature of the loading. As the load is increased, therefore, the bar forces always stand

29

in the same relation to each other and to the applied load, no matter how the material behaves. Thus in this example, each bar force is always equal to 0.5 *W*, at working load and beyond, right to the point of failure.

There is a simple rule by which we can identify a statically determinate structure like that shown in Fig. 3.1a. In all its parts it has only just enough members, constraints between members, and supports, to preserve its shape and keep it stable and at rest under load. If any one member, constraint, or support is removed, the structure collapses, i.e. undergoes a major change of shape. Figs. 3.1b, c, and d illustrate this. The frame shown in Fig. 3.2 can easily be demonstrated by this test to be statically determinate. If any one of the bars—EB, for example—fails, the part to the right of it swings downwards as a mechanism, as shown at (b).

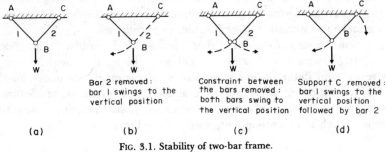

(a)

(b) Bar 2 removed: bar 1 swings to the vertical position

(c) Constraint between the bars removed: both bars swing to the vertical position

(d) Support C removed: bar 1 swings to the vertical position followed by bar 2

FIG. 3.1. Stability of two-bar frame.

The addition of a vertical bar to the two-bar frame of Fig. 3.1 converts it to a statically indeterminate structure (Fig. 3.3a), the special characteristic of which (as the name implies) is that the forces in the various parts do not depend only on the laws of statics, but also on the relative stiffnesses of the members. In this particular structure under a vertical load at B, and with linear-elastic behaviour throughout the material of the bars, the stress in the vertical bar must be twice as great as in the others. The proportion of *W* carried by this bar must therefore increase as its cross-sectional area increases in relation to that of the other two. We can see this intuitively if we take two extreme cases, and imagine the central bar to be, firstly, very thick, and then very thin in

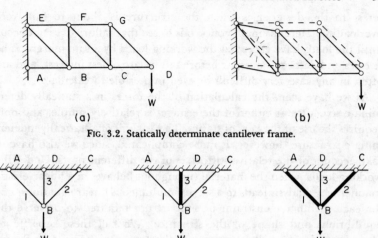

FIG. 3.2. Statically determinate cantilever frame.

Bar 3 very thick
compared with others:
it carries nearly all
the load

Bar 3 very thin
compared with others:
it carries hardly
any load

(a)   (b)   (c)

FIG. 3.3. Statically indeterminate three-bar frame.

comparison with the others (Figs. 3.3b and c). Common sense tells us that in the first case practically all the load will be carried by this bar, and in the second case virtually none. It is, in fact, a general structural truth that in all statically indeterminate structures an increase in the stiffness at any point tends to attract force to that point and to draw it away from other parts; conversely, a weakening or loss of stiffness in any part causes the force in that part to diminish in proportion to the forces elsewhere.

The engineer is especially interested in structural behaviour at two stages. The first is when the structure carries the loads or other forces expected in service (these are known as the working loads). Here he is primarily concerned to make sure that the calculated stresses are kept well within the elastic limit of the material, and that the deformations are also within well-defined limits. The second stage of particular interest to the designer is when the structure is about to fail from overloading. Here his main concern is to see that failure does not occur until the loads have exceeded the working loads by a safe margin. The stresses and deformations just before failure are of less interest, and are often in any case very difficult or even impossible to calculate.

As we have seen, the calculation of the forces in a statically determinate structure at either of these stages is relatively simple, and only requires the use of the laws of statics. The analysis of a statically indeterminate structure, however, is more complicated, since we also have to take account of the relative stiffnesses of the different parts. Under the working loads, when the material throughout behaves in a linear-elastic manner, the analysis leads to a set of simultaneous linear equations, one for each member, constraint or support not required to preserve the equilibrium and shape of the structure. We call these superfluous elements *redundant*. In the very simple structure of Fig. 3.3, for instance, there is only one redundant member and therefore only one equation, which expresses the fact that when the structure is loaded and the bars change in length, they must continue to fit together at B. But the number of redundants increases rapidly with the complexity of the structure; even the fairly elementary pin-jointed truss of Fig. 3.4 contains six redundant members, for example. Until the advent of modern

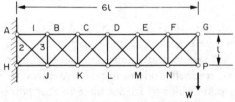

FIG. 3.4. Cantilever truss with six redundant members.

digital computers the solution of a set of as few as six simultaneous equations was a slow process, and various ingenious techniques were invented by structural analysts to simplify manual solution. Nowadays, provided a suitable computer is at hand, the analysis of structures with hundreds of redundants presents no particular difficulties; standard programmes are at the engineer's disposal, and he does not even need to be expert in statically indeterminate structural theory to get a solution in a matter of minutes, once the information on the characteristics of the structure and the loads has been fed into the programme.

This is only possible, however, at working load, when the behaviour of the structure is linear-elastic. Once yielding has started, analysis becomes much more difficult. Mathematically, the equations are now non-linear. Fortunately, non-linear analysis is seldom needed, at least by the designing engineer.

Collapse

At the point of collapse of a statically indeterminate structure, analysis is once again relatively simple because, provided the parts which yield are ductile enough to remain intact until a mechanism has developed, the structure is statically determinate, at least in the section involved in the mechanism. For example, in the frame of Fig. 3.3a, suppose that bar 3 is the first to reach its ultimate load F_{u3}, and then goes on extending plastically, i.e. at constant force, as W is increased further. Since the force in one bar from now on is known, and the structure was originally once redundant, the forces in the other bars can now be determined by statics in terms of W. After a further increase in W the force in a second bar, say 1, reaches its ultimate strength F_{u1}. It is now possible to find by statics the value of W needed to reach this stage, at which point bars 1 and 3 begin to extend plastically until one breaks and the other immediately does also, leaving bar 2 to swing about point C as a mechanism.

Most mechanisms of collapse are usually a good deal more complicated than this, and they are sometimes difficult to identify. Usually the structure can collapse in several different alternative ways. The load at which collapse occurs in each mode is determined by statics, and the actual failure load will naturally be the smallest. For example, in the frame of Fig. 3.4, failure of bars 1 and 2 would produce a mechanism in which the entire frame to the right of AH swings about joint H (Fig. 3.5). By taking moments about this joint, and recognizing that the load W_u is tending to overturn the frame while rotation is being resisted by the forces in the two bars 1 and 2, we find that

$$W_u \cdot 6\ell = F_{u1} \cdot \ell + F_{u2} \cdot 0.707\ell$$

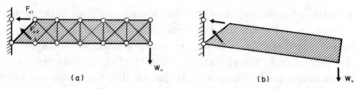

FIG. 3.5. Collapse of truss of Fig. 3.4 by failure of bars 1 and 2.

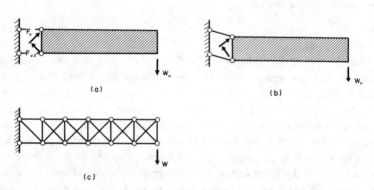

FIG. 3.6. Collapse of truss of Fig. 3.4 by failure of bars 2 and 3.

which gives the value of W_u. It is worth noting that the structure *as a whole* is still five times redundant, but the collapse analysis is a static one. Another mechanism (one of a number in this particular structure) would develop (Fig. 3.6) if the two diagonals in the panel ABJH failed (AJ in tension and HB in compression). Again, W_u can be found by statics in terms of the ultimate strengths of the two bars.

In both these modes of failure the remainder of the structure is still highly redundant, and some members may have yielded or even reached their ultimate strength. In general it is impossible to calculate the forces in the members at the point of collapse, but, as was mentioned earlier, the designer does not need this information. The attainment of a calculated collapse load does depend, however, on the members which have yielded being ductile enough not to fail prematurely. Except in very simple structures with idealized material (the structure discussed in Chapter 2 — see Fig. 2.3 — was a case in point) the required amount of ductility cannot be calculated: in the absence of tests to failure on prototypes of his project structure, the engineer must rely on past experience, careful design, and control of the quality of his material.

Partly because of the difficulty and intellectual challenge of statically indeterminate linear structural analysis, most recent textbooks on the theory of structures deal mainly with this subject, and it forms what some people consider to be an excessively large part of structural engineering courses. This has led to a widely held if subconscious impression in the minds of students and young engineers that highly redundant structures are in some way inherently superior to statically determinate ones. A high degree of redundancy is unavoidable in many types of structure — multi-storey building frames are an example — and it has certain merits which we will look at in more detail in a later chapter, but these are unrelated to complexity of analysis. One important advantage which is often claimed is that a redundant structure gives warning of the approach of failure by yielding or cracking in some part, which in turn produces an increasing rate of deflection with addition of load. This was the case in the three-bar structure discussed in Chapter 2. But if the effect of the redundancy does not extend throughout the structure, failure can be as abrupt as in a statically determinate structure. For example, the truss of Fig. 3.6c has a redundant member in every panel but the one nearest the wall. If a member in this panel fails, the truss as a whole collapses immediately. Nevertheless, redundancy does give the designer the opportunity to ensure that there is some advance warning of approaching failure.

Possibly the ready access nowadays to computer programs for the analysis of highly redundant structures will remove some of the mystery that still surrounds the subject, and put statically determinate analysis and behaviour in better perspective.

Cable or Chain Structures

Hanging bridges made from jungle vines and creepers were almost certainly the earliest man-made structures of any size. By 1500 B.C. iron was being made in primitive forges in India, and suspension bridges with wrought-iron links or chains were probably in existence well before the beginning of the Christian era. The earliest description of an iron suspension bridge in the European literature appears in *Machinae Novae*, a book published by Faustus Verantius in 1607 (Fig. 3.7). Ropes

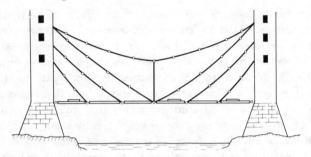

FIG. 3.7. Iron suspension bridge illustrated by Verantius (1607).

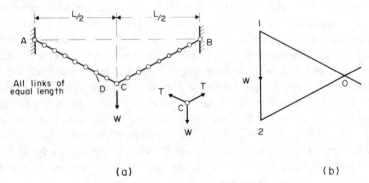

(a)   (b)

FIG. 3.8. Chain carrying central vertical load.

were used for military bridging at least from A. D. 1600. From the earliest times, in fact, the principle of the suspension bridge has been pre-eminent for the largest spans, mainly because it exploits the tensile strength of natural fibres and iron and steel with a simplicity and efficiency unrivalled by any other structural form.

Figure 3.8a shows a very simple example of a suspension structure, not unlike the upper part of Verantius's bridge. The sixteen iron links, all of the same length, are connected by pins, and a load W hangs from the central pin. If we assume that the weight of the links is very small compared with the load they carry, the two halves will be pulled straight. The pin to which the load is attached is acted on by three forces, the load and the two pulls T from the sides, and is in equilibrium under these forces. We can therefore draw a triangle of forces 012 (Fig.

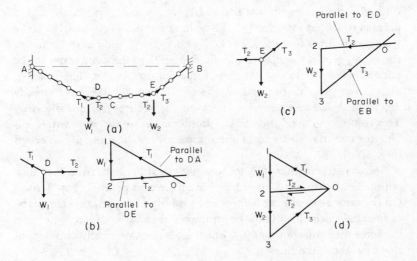

FIG. 3.9. Chain carrying two vertical loads.

3.8b), starting with the line 12 representing W to some scale, and then drawing two lines 10 and 20 parallel to the two sides to intersect at 0. The length of the lines 10 and 20 gives the tensions in the two sides: from the symmetry of the structure they are the same.

This is the simplest possible example of a statically determinate analysis. The solution is based only on the equilibrium of the pin C carrying the load, and is not affected by the elastic properties of the chain, except that we assume that its extension under the tensions T is too small to change the geometry of the system appreciably from that in the unstrained condition.

We can go a step further, and hang two loads W_1 and W_2 from pins at points D and E on the chain (Fig. 3.9a). Tensions T_1, T_2, and T_3 will be set up in the three parts of the chain, and our problem is to determine their magnitudes from a knowledge of the shape taken up by the chain.* First, the pin at point D is in equilibrium under the three forces W_1, T_1, and T_2, and we can draw a triangle of forces as we did in the first problem: we draw a line 12 to represent W_1 to some scale, and then

---

*Not so easy to calculate as one might think, but we assume that we know the shape.

through 1 draw a line 10 parallel to DA, and another line 20 through 2 parallel to DE, as shown at (b). These lines intersect at 0, and 120 is the triangle of forces for the pin at D. The lengths of the lines 10 and 20, therefore, give us the magnitudes of T_1 and T_2 to the same scale. In the same way we can draw a triangle of forces for the pin at E. This is shown at (c), and gives us the magnitudes of T_3 and T_2. We have already determined T_2, so we have a check on the accuracy of our drawing. This completes the solution to the problem, but we can if we wish combine the two triangles to form one compact *force diagram*, as it is called (Fig. 3.9d).

Going a step further still, let us hang equal loads W from four pins symmetrically disposed on either side of the mid point C (Fig. 3.10a). On the same reasoning as before, and assuming that we know the shape of the chain, which will now be symmetrical about midspan, we obtain the force diagram shown at (b), which is also symmetrically disposed, in this case about the line 30.

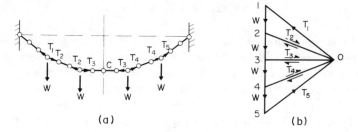

FIG. 3.10. Chain carrying four equal vertical loads.

Now let us place equal weights w at each of the pins in the chain (Fig. 3.11a). Again the chain will hang symmetrically about the midpoint C, and the force diagram, shown at (b), will also be symmetrically shaped. In this particular case we can deduce the shape of the chain. Each inclined line or *ray* in the force diagram gives not only the magnitude of the force in the corresponding link but also its inclination. Starting from midspan, we can see, therefore, that the slope of the links, measured as the tangent of the angle of inclination to the horizontal, increases in proportion to the horizontal distance from midspan. Now the curve whose slope varies in this way is a parabola: the chain therefore takes up

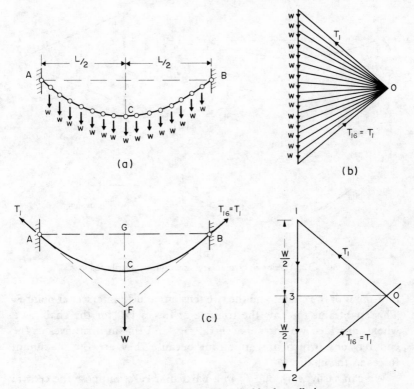

FIG. 3.11. Chain carrying equal vertical loads at all pins.

a parabolic shape. In stating this we assume that the sag of the chain is small in comparison with its span, so that the horizontal projection of each link is virtually the same: in fact, it diminishes slightly towards the sides because of the slope of the links.

Since the slope varies in this way, the slope at the sides is twice the average slope, so that if tangents are drawn at the ends A and B they will intersect at a point F twice as far below the ends as the mid-point C of the chain (Fig. 3.11c). If we now look at the equilibrium of the chain as a whole, it is acted on by the tensions T_1 and T_{16} (which is equal to T_1) at its ends and by the weights w. Supposing that all the weights add up to a total of W, then this resultant weight acts down through the

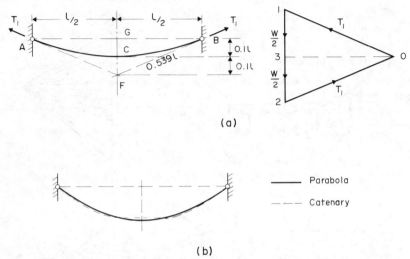

(a)

(b)

FIG. 3.12. Tension in chain carrying uniformly distributed load.

mid-point of the chain, and the two tensions and W intersect at point F. This enables us to draw the triangle of forces 120 for the chain as a whole, provided we know its central sag, and this in turn gives us the end tensions, which are important because they are the maximum forces in the chain.

We can easily work out T_1 in a particular case. Suppose the central dip d is one-tenth of the span 1. Then in Fig. 3.12, $GF = 0.21$, and FB is therefore equal to 0.5391. Now the triangles GFB and 320 are similar, so that:

$$\frac{FB}{GF} = \frac{20}{32}$$

and since 32 equals $W/2$ we have:

$$\frac{T}{W/2} = \frac{0.5391}{0.21}$$

from which

$$T = 1.35W$$

We can work out roughly how large a span a cable of uniform cross-section and of this shape can attain before it breaks under its own weight, for this weight is distributed uniformly along the cable in the same way as the weights w were spaced along the chain, and the cable will assume a similar shape. The length of the cable is approximately 1 (more correctly it is 1.02671) and if its cross-sectional area is A the weight W equals $1A\rho$, where ρ is the density of the material. Then

$$T = 1.35W = 1.35\ 1A\rho.$$

The maximum stress σ in the cable is equal to $T/A = 1.351\rho$, and the cable breaks when $\sigma = \sigma_u$, the ultimate tensile strength; that is, when

$$\sigma_u = 1.351\rho$$

and hence when

$$1 = \frac{1.35\sigma_u}{\rho} = 1.35S$$ where S is the specific strength of the material.

From the Table in Chapter 2 the value of S for high-strength steel pre-stressing wire, which is similar to some cable material, is 26,700 m, so that for this grade of wire

$$1 = 1.35 \cdot 26,700 = 36,045 \text{ m.}$$

If the cable supports a highway or railway bridge it has to carry a deck and traffic in addition to its own weight, and there must also be a margin of safety against failure. The practical limit to a suspension span of this shape is, therefore, much smaller than this figure, but it is still well beyond what has been achieved so far, which is less than 1500 m.

A uniform cable or chain hanging under its own weight actually assumes a shape called a catenary, which is slightly different from a parabola of the same span and dip. This is because the latter is the curve taken up by a weightless string or chain carrying a load which is uniform for each small unit of the *horizontal* span, which was our assumption in our analysis of the chain with weights w at each pin, whereas the weight of a cable per unit of horizontal span increases towards the sides owing to the increasing slope of the cable. Because of this, for a given length of cable the catenary is slightly lower than the parabola towards the sides and slightly higher near midspan (Fig. 3.12b). We used the parabola because it is much easier to calculate than the catenary; the difference between the two curves is negligible for our purposes for this ratio of dip to span.

Chains and cables were the first structures to be analysed by the early workers in statics. Simon Stevin, who was the first to formulate, in a book on statics published in Holland in 1586, some of the basic concepts of the subject, including the triangle of forces, carried out experiments on loaded strings; and by 1691 the Swiss mathematician James Bernoulli had derived the equation to the catenary.

Arches

Now let us return to the simplest of the chain structures considered earlier (Fig. 3.8) and suppose that each half consists of a single link or bar (Fig. 3.13a). The force T in each bar is the same as before. If we reverse the direction of the load W, making it act upwards instead of downwards, as shown at (b), T is also reversed in direction, becoming compressive instead of tensile, but its magnitude remains the same. This structure is best looked at upside down, as at (c), and we now see that it is a very simple arch.

The chain of Fig. 3.9 can likewise be taken as consisting of three bars (Fig. 3.14a) and can be put into reverse in the same way to give the arch shown at (b). The forces T_1, T_2, and T_3 in the three bars have the same magnitudes as in the chain structure, but are compressive instead of

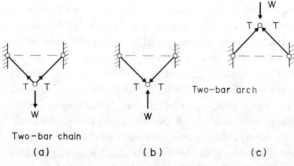

FIG. 3.13. Two-bar linear arch.

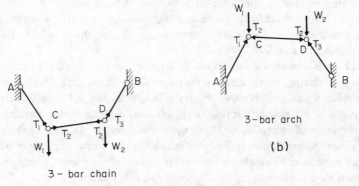

FIG. 3.14. Three-bar linear arch.

tensile. In fact, a weightless chain or cable loaded in any way whatever has its exact counterpart in a weightless arch of precisely the same shape and carrying the same loads. The internal forces are the same at all points, but are compressive in the arch whereas they are tensile in the chain. If the parts of the arch have weight, this is simply regarded as a load at the various points.

If, then, the shape of the arch is such that when all the loads on it, including its own weight, are applied to a string or chain of the same length the string assumes the same shape, the thrust in the arch acts along the axis of the members at all points. Because of this such an arch is called a linear arch. The shape is also called *funicular*, from the Latin word for rope (*funiculus*).

The important fact that the forces in an arch can be deduced from those in a chain of the same shape was recognized very early in the history of structural analysis. It was first realized by Robert Hooke, who is also famous for his law expressing the linear relation between tension and extension in elastic bodies (first stated in a Latin anagram published in 1675) and for inventions such as the spring added to the balance wheel of timekeepers. In another Latin anagram announced by Hooke at the same time, whose translation soon became known, he stated (in modern idiom) that: "As hangs a flexible cable, so, inverted, stand the touching pieces of an arch". H. J. Hopkins, in his book *A Span of Bridges*, gives a fascinating account of Hooke's discovery and his extension of the idea to the three-dimensional equivalent of the arch, the dome. There seems little doubt that Hooke was of material assistance to Sir Christopher Wren during the design of the dome of St. Paul's Cathedral in London.

There is one vitally important difference between the behaviour of a cable or chain and that of the corresponding linear arch. A change in the relative values of W_1 and W_2 in the linkage of Fig. 3.14a only causes it to move into a new and stable configuration. But the slightest alteration in the value of either W_1 or W_2 in the arch of Fig. 3.14b leads to collapse as a mechanism. This tendency to instability and abrupt failure is latent in all structures in which the internal forces are compressive, and we shall return to it repeatedly in the discussion in this chapter.

In this particular arch we can prevent collapse by making one of the joints (C, for example) rigid in some way, say by tightening up the pin or by welding the two bars together. They then act as a single bar with a kink in it, and the arch is obviously stable (Fig. 3.15a). Doing this makes

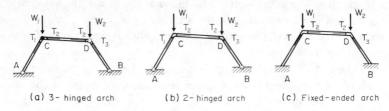

(a) 3- hinged arch   (b) 2- hinged arch   (c) Fixed-ended arch

FIG. 3.15. Examples of linear arches: the forces T_1, T_2, and T_3 are the same in each case.

no difference to the forces in the various parts; each still has the same value as in the corresponding cable structure, and the line of thrust is still along the arch axis at every point. Because of the correspondence with the cable, the internal forces are statically determinate.

This structure is known as a three-hinged arch. It is in any case statically determinate, as we can check from our test: we cannot remove either member or any support condition without causing collapse. But we can go a step further, and make the joint D rigid as well, again without affecting in any way the internal forces. This structure (known as a two-hinged arch) is normally statically indeterminate, but for this particular loading condition (and for this one only) the internal forces can be found by considering the statics of the corresponding cable structure. We can even fix all four pins, which makes the arch a fixed or encastré arch. (Fig. 3.15c), again without causing any change in the internal forces, though this structure is normally three times statically indeterminate. These three structures and the one illustrated in Fig. 3.14b are all examples of linear arches.

There is one approximation in the foregoing argument which the reader may already have observed. The bars will shorten a little under load, and the angles between them, and the general configuration of the arch, will change slightly. Taking the fixed arch of Fig. 3.15c, for example, if we assume that it has the correct shape for a linear arch when it is unloaded, then when we apply the loads the angles between the members and the slope of the arch at each support will tend to alter slightly, but will be prevented from doing so by the fixity of the joints. Bending stresses will thus be set up in the arch which will be additional to the direct stresses caused by the axial forces which we have been considering. These "secondary" stresses, as they are called, have only a slight effect on the magnitude of the direct forces, unless the members are very thick and stocky in relation to the over-all dimensions of the arch.

It must be emphasized again that the argument applies only for the set of loads which produces this particular shape of cable. If, for instance, the fixed arch carried a single load W (Fig. 3.16) the line of thrust would be similar to that shown in Fig. 3.13a, as in the cable structure corresponding to this loading. But this cannot fit the axis of this arch. It does so as well as it can, keeping as closely as possible to the axis, but inevitably deviates from it, and this causes bending in the members as well as direct compression, and a considerable increase in the stresses. Furthermore, they cannot now be calculated by statics.

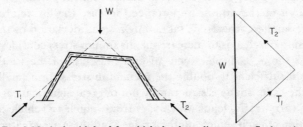

FIG. 3.16. Arch with load for which the thrust line cannot fit the axis.

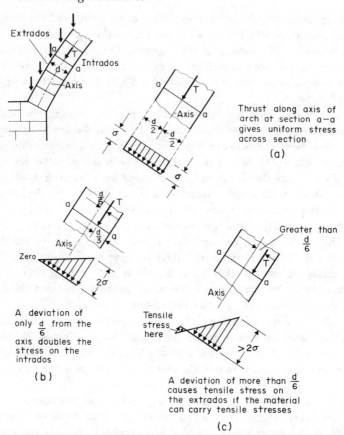

Extrados

Intrados

Axis

a

a

d

T

Thrust along axis of
arch at section a—a
gives uniform stress
across section

(a)

A deviation of
only d from the
     6
axis doubles the
stress on the
intrados

(b)

Zero

2σ

Greater than
d
6

Tensile
stress
here

>2σ

A deviation of more than $\frac{d}{6}$
causes tensile stress on
the extrados if the material
can carry tensile stresses

(c)

FIG. 3.17. Increase in maximum stress when the thrust line deviates from the arch axis.

For the designer, Hooke's "line of an arch for supporting any weight assigned" is of the utmost importance, because the linear arch shape gives the smallest stresses. It takes only a small deviation of the thrust line from the arch axis to increase the maximum stress considerably. As Fig. 3.17 shows, a displacement of only one-sixth of the width of the arch rib is sufficient to double the maximum stress. In a small arched bridge the exact shape is structurally not of great significance, because it has to carry traffic loads which vary from vehicle to vehicle and with the position of each vehicle on the bridge, and these are greater than its own weight. There is therefore no one linear arch shape which the engineer might reasonably select for his design. But the weight of a very large arched bridge accounts for nearly all the load: the effect of traffic is insignificant by comparison. And, as we saw in Chapter 2, as the size of a structure increases, there comes a point at which it is incapable of carrying even its own weight however well it is designed. It is therefore essential that the axis of the arch should conform as closely as possible to the funicular shape for the dead weight of the arch. The largest concrete arched bridge yet built, at Gladesville, N.S.W., Australia, with a span of 1000 feet or 305 m, was designed on this principle (Fig. 3.18).

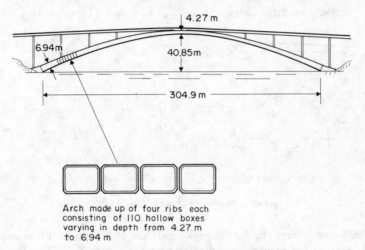

Arch made up of four ribs each
consisting of 110 hollow boxes
varying in depth from 4.27 m
to 6.94 m

FIG. 3.18. Gladesville Bridge, Sydney, Australia.

As we saw earlier, a cable of uniform cross-section hanging under its own weight takes the form of a catenary, which is slightly different from the parabola; and so the ideal shape for an arch of uniform thickness which only has to carry its own weight is also a catenary. The barrel-vaulted arched roof at Ctesiphon, Iraq (built about 220 B.C. of mud bricks) is approximately of this form (Fig. 3.19).

Though the principle of the arch was understood by the early Mesopotamian and Egyptian builders, neither they nor the Greeks used it to any extent except in minor construction like underground culverts.

FIG. 3.19. Barrel vault roof of the Taq-e Kisra Palace, Ctesiphon, Iraq.

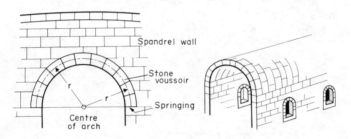

FIG. 3.20. Roman arch and barrel vault.

The Romans were the first to make wide use of arches, and it is one of the reasons for their outstanding success as constructors. The Roman arch and its counterpart in buildings, the barrel vault, were almost invariably semicircular in shape (Fig. 3.20). Undoubtedly this was because the circle is by far the easiest shape to set out: if the arch was of uniform thickness, as was usually the case, each stone or voussoir was bounded by two concentric circles and two radii all related to the same central point. As Hopkins points out, so important was this centre in Roman and later arch construction that the framework used for supporting an arch during erection is still called *centering*.

The semicircular arch corresponds to a cable subjected to a uniform radial pressure (Fig. 3.21). This is a form of loading roughly similar under certain conditions to the earth pressure on a deep culvert. The

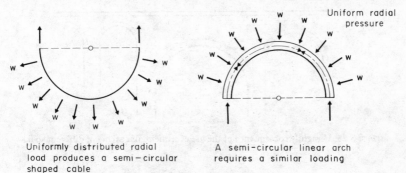

Uniformly distributed radial load produces a semi-circular shaped cable

A semi-circular linear arch requires a similar loading

FIG. 3.21. Linear semicircular arch.

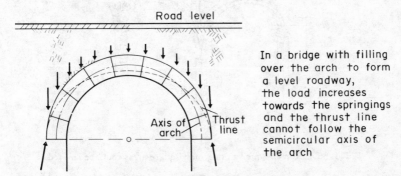

Road level

In a bridge with filling over the arch to form a level roadway, the load increases towards the springings and the thrust line cannot follow the semicircular axis of the arch

Axis of arch   Thrust line

FIG. 3.22. Non-linear semicircular arch.

thrust at the supports or springings of the arch is then vertical in direction. In buildings and bridges, however, the loading is usually quite different (Fig. 3.22), and the thrust line cannot possibly follow the axis of the arch, though it tries to do so as closely as it can. In particular, the thrusts at the springings are inclined to the vertical and tend to spread the abutments apart. The Romans may have adopted the semicircle instead of a smaller segment of a circle in the belief that the end thrusts *would* be vertical: if so, their misapprehension was excusable, for pseudo-learned disputation on this point was still going on in the seventeenth century.

When after the Dark Ages interest revived in the science and art of the ancient world, it was natural for Roman forms of construction to be

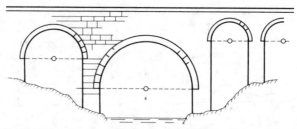

FIG. 3.23. Unsightly consequence of the use of semicircular arches of different spans.

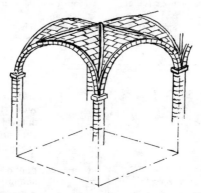

FIG. 3.24. Romanesque vaulting: only square areas could be covered.

followed again, and the semicircular arch and vault were adopted in the style of architecture known as the Romanesque. But the semicircle places severe restrictions on the designer, since the rise of such an arch is always half the span. In a bridge with unequal spans this means that either the crowns or the springings of the arches must be at different levels, which can be unsightly (Fig. 3.23). In buildings more serious difficulties arise. The Romanesque barrel vault required continuous support, and when used for the roof of a church made the interior very dark (Fig. 3.20). The development of the groined vault with semicircular arches (Fig. 3.24) did enable light to enter from all sides, but because of the rigid proportions of the semicircle it was only possible to cover square bays in this way.

The remarkable achievements of the Gothic period of architecture are due in large part to the use from about A.D. 1140 onwards of the

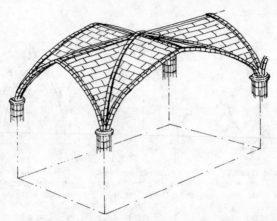

FIG. 3.25. Gothic vaulting: rectangular areas could be covered.

pointed arch. By varying the ratio of rise to span of the arches in vaulting, it was now possible to cover rectangular as well as square bays (Fig. 3.25). Window openings could be made as tall and slender as desired, and architectural planning took on a new freedom. A tall pointed arch exerts a smaller lateral thrust on its supports than a semicircular one, and columns and buttresses became more and more unsubstantial as the emphasis on verticality was increased.

Since, however, an abrupt kink in a weightless cable implies a concentrated weight at the kink, it follows that for the thrust in the pointed arch of Gothic construction to be linear, i.e. to pass along the axis of the arch at all points, there should be a substantial concentrated load at the apex as well as a distributed load along the two sides (Fig. 3.26). A good example of the correct use of a pointed arch can be seen in the Font Pédrouse viaduct in France (Fig. 3.27). But this condition was hardly ever present in Gothic building, and in a pointed arch with thin ribs the thrust line under its own weight (Fig. 3.26c) can hardly be kept within the thickness of the arch. Such an arch will not stand up on its own without support from the adjoining masonry, and this must often have caused difficulties during construction.

In dry or weakly jointed stone arches there is always the possibility of collapse. We saw in Fig. 3.17 that a movement of the thrust line from the axis of only one-sixth of the width of the rib is sufficient to double

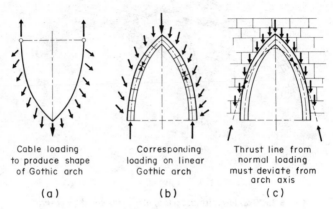

Cable loading to produce shape of Gothic arch

(a)

Corresponding loading on linear Gothic arch

(b)

Thrust line from normal loading must deviate from arch axis

(c)

FIG. 3.26. Linear and non-linear Gothic arches.

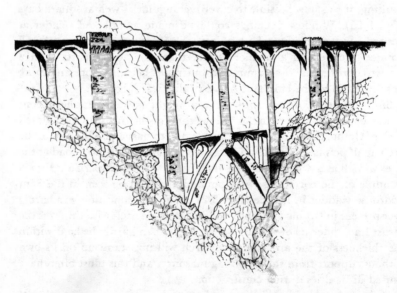

FIG. 3.27. Font Pédrouse Viaduct, Pyrenées Orientales, France.

the compressive stress on the edge towards which the thrust moves, and reduce it to zero at the other edge. Further movement of the thrust line increases still more the stress at the inner edge; and if it actually passes outside the width of the rib the joint nearest this point opens out and the voussoirs tend to hinge about the inner edge. Thus the thrust need deviate only a small distance from the axis to cause a dramatic increase in the stresses in the arch and even, under certain circumstances, to contribute to its collapse.

These circumstances were clearly recognized by the Frenchman Danisy in 1732 when he described experiments he had carried out on model arches (Fig. 3.28) which were later used by his countryman Coulomb in formulating rules for the design of arches. What Danisy observed can be explained by reference to the stone arch of Fig. 3.29. The thrust line due to the weight of the voussoirs passes through the arch as shown at (a), and since it lies within the arch everywhere there is no danger of collapse, though the arch is not a linear one. Now suppose that a load P is added as shown at (b). The thrust line develops a peak under the load, and as P increases this peak sharpens and the two sides of the thrust line straighten. One of the remarkable things about structures is that they do their best to resist failure as long as possible. The thrust line adjusts its position so as to keep inside the arch everywhere. But as P gets greater the line becomes more and more triangular in shape until it touches the extrados or outside of the arch (see Fig. 3.17a) at the load. Assuming that the joints have no tensile strength—this is certainly a fair assumption for Roman and mediaeval arch construction, which was either dry or jointed in weak mortar—the joint A under the load opens very slightly. With further increase in the value of P the thrust line reaches the extrados or intrados successively at three other points, B, C, and D, the sequence and the location of the points depending on the shape of the arch and the loading. When the last point is reached, the arch, which already possesses three hinges and is therefore statically determinate, like the structure of Fig. 3.15a, develops a fourth. The slightest further change in load now produces collapse as a mechanism.

The value of the load P to cause failure can be worked out by various methods based on the laws of statics. One way is to guess a value, draw trial thrust lines and see if one can be found which lies inside the arch

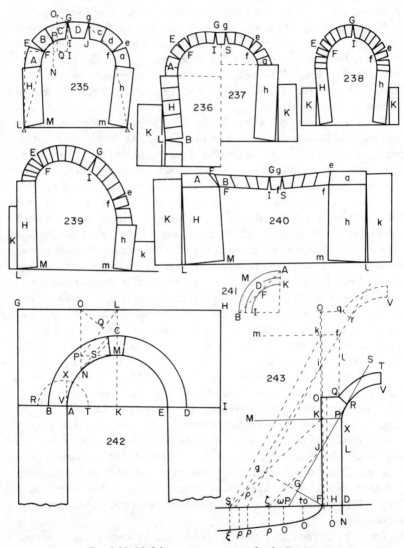

FIG. 3.28. Model tests on masonry arches by Danisy.

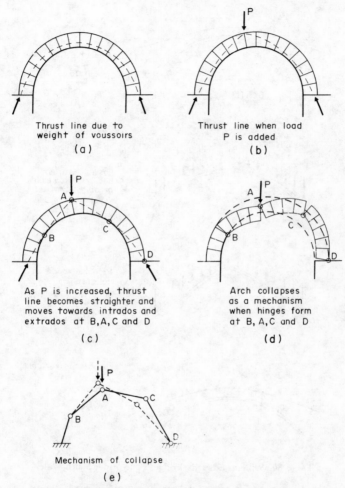

FIG. 3.29. Possible mode of collapse of masonry voussoir arch.

everywhere and does not touch the extrados or intrados at more than four points. This is a laborious process of trial and error, but it was the only one available for designers until late in the nineteenth century.

The story of a famous stone bridge built in 1756 in Pontypridd, South Wales, and still standing, well illustrates the importance of the thrust

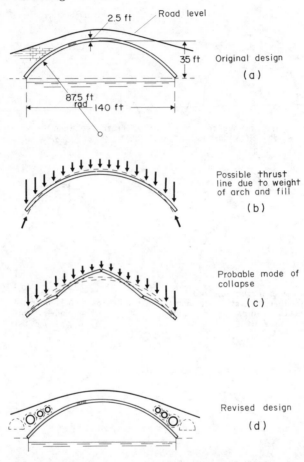

FIG. 3.30. William Edwards' bridge, Pontypridd, South Wales.

line. This segmental arch has a clear span of 43 m and a rib thickness of only 0.76 m, half the normal width for a bridge of this size built in those days (Fig. 3.30a). There was thus very little room for manoeuvre in the location of the thrust line. To reduce the approach gradients there was a considerable depth of fill over the haunches, and while this was being placed after the arch centering had been removed, the haunches of the rib moved inwards, the crown was pushed up and the arch collapsed into the river. The great weight of fill near the sides had caused the thrust line to be sharply curved in these regions, and it could not be accommodated within the thickness of the rib (Fig. 3.30b). In consequence the arch collapsed, probably by developing a five-hinge mechanism, as shown at (c). The builder, a local mason, redesigned the bridge with three circular culverts and a semicircular arch (the latter hidden by the side walls) on each side, as shown at (d), and this was sufficient, though he may not have fully understood why, to lighten the load on the haunches enough to bring the thrust line completely within the arch rib.

Under the working loads it is obviously not enough to ensure that a thrust line can be found which lies within the arch rib everywhere. This only guarantees that these loads will not cause failure. For there to be a margin of safety against collapse in service it must be possible to find a thrust line for the working loads *multiplied by some factor* of, say, two or so which lies wholly within the arch.

In the nineteenth century the more usual approach was to ensure that the arch would not crack anywhere while in service. A glance at Fig. 3.17c shows that if the thrust at any section where the width of the rib is d is more than $d/6$ away from the axis tensile stress will develop at one edge. So long, therefore, as the thrust stays within the middle third of the width of the rib everywhere the stress will be wholly compressive (Fig. 3.31). This is an exacting requirement, and it led to very conservative designs. A semicircular arch, for example, will not satisfy it even under its own weight alone unless the voussoirs are very thick in proportion to the span. But tensile stress and cracking between two voussoirs does not necessarily mean that collapse is near. As we saw a little earlier, the arch must be about to open out at three joints before failure is imminent.

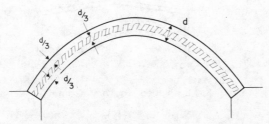

FIG. 3.31. "Middle-third" rule for the design of arches.

The maximum span to which a stone arch can be built before it crushes under its own weight can be found in the same way as was done for cable spans. For an arch of parabolic shape with a central rise of 10 per cent of the span, the maximum possible span is the same, i.e. 1.35 S, which for granite gives us a figure of 7000 × 1.35 or 9450 m. Of course, this is a purely hypothetical result, for long before such a span was reached an arch of practicable proportions would have buckled and failed under its own weight.

Nowadays, small-span arches are usually made of steel or of reinforced or prestressed concrete, which have tensile as well as compressive strength, and they are often designed in shapes very different from the linear arch form. They have to support a variety of loads which are greater than their own weights, so that no one ideal shape can be found. The shape is usually governed more by functional than by structural requirements: clearance in a portal frame bridge carrying one road over another (Fig. 3.32a), or the need for a sloping roof in a factory frame (Fig. 3.32b).

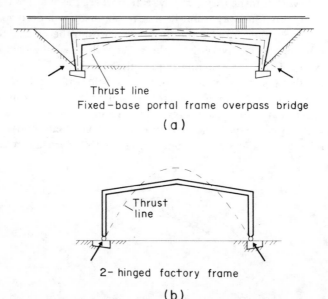

Thrust line
Fixed-base portal frame overpass bridge

(a)

Thrust line
2-hinged factory frame

(b)

FIG. 3.32. Thrust line in bridge and factory frames.

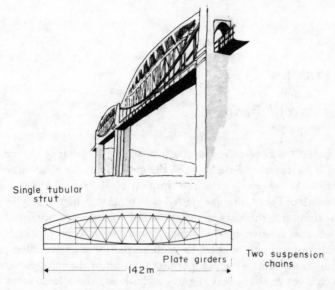

FIG. 3.33. Saltash Bridge, Plymouth, U.K.

Very few designers have used the arch and cable in combination, yet this is a logical solution to the problem of spanning a gap, especially where the supports cannot resist outward thrust. The arch pushes out and the cable pulls in, and if the two are combined in a single structure one can be made to balance the other. This was the solution found by the brilliant Victorian engineer I. K. Brunel to the problem at Saltash in Devon, where the railway bridge over the Tamar river is poised far above the water, and there was no possibility of resisting the outward thrust of arches. This great structure, completed in 1859 as Brunel was dying, worn out by worry, enormous responsibilities, and overwork at the age of 53, has two main spans each of 142 m (Fig. 3.33). The trusses in each span are a combination of a tubular wrought-iron arch and a suspension chain braced together with light wrought-iron web members to form a single trussed beam. For the period the scale of the construction, like that of the Britannia railway bridge by Brunel's friend Robert Stephenson (Fig. 7.7), is staggering: the tubes are oval in cross-section, 3.7 m high by 5.1 m wide—big enough to take a railway train inside them.

CHAPTER 4

Trusses and Beams

THE EASIEST way of relieving the supports of an arch of the outward thrust is by inserting a tie between the ends. Thus the elementary arch of Fig. 3.13c is converted to the simplest of all trusses, the triangular framework of Fig. 4.1a. The tie AB is in tension, which is usually given a plus sign, and the sloping rafters are of course in compression. This kind of truss is often used to support small roofs. The proper form of statically determinate support for such a structure is a frictionless pinned bearing at one end A, which permits rotation of the joint there as the truss changes its shape very slightly under load, and a frictionless roller bearing at B, which enables the tie to extend or contract as the stress in

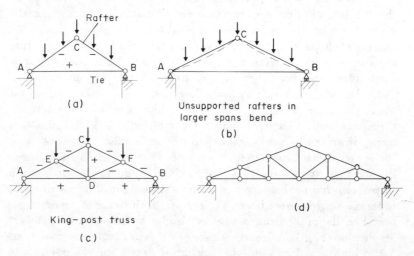

FIG. 4.1. Development of roof trusses.

60

it or its temperature alters, as well as permitting the joint B to rotate. In practice a small timber or steel truss is bolted down at one support and allowed to slide at the other, but in large bridge and roof trusses great care is taken to ensure that the bearings really do work as they should. Formerly they were expensive items in high-strength steel and bearing metal, but nowadays quite large spans are supported on thick pads of elastomeric plastic, which are cheaper and need virtually no maintenance.

As the span of a roof truss gets bigger, the weight of the roof distributed along the rafters causes bending (Fig. 4.1b) and to reduce this inclined props may be inserted as shown at (c). The tie cannot resist the downward component of the thrust in these props, however, and a vertical tie traditionally called a kingpost is added. Timber kingpost trusses were used in churches for centuries. When wrought-iron bars became readily available, the tie and the kingpost were often made of this material; it was lighter and tensile connections were more easily made than in timber.

For larger spans still, one may add further props and vertical ties, as at (d). Alternatively, one can go back to the linear arch for the loads on the roof and add a tie (Fig. 4.2a). If the loads are equal and equally spaced across the span the arch is parabolic. But it is highly unstable if it consists merely of a number of bars pinned together, and it must be braced by some system of web members in the space between the arch and the tie, as shown at (b). These members are unstressed unless the loading on the roof changes from that corresponding to the shape of the linear arch, but they are essential for the stability of the framework. This type of truss is called a bowstring truss, from the resemblance to the archer's bow, and is often used for bridges as well as for factory roofs. In a bridge the traffic loads pass along at the level of the tie, and the vertical ties are then essential to transmit these loads to the arch rib. Bowstring trusses are sometimes seen in reverse (Fig. 4.2c). These are less common because they can cause difficulty with headroom underneath, but they are very economical because the arch members are in tension and therefore do not have to be designed against failure by buckling, a problem which we will look at in a later chapter.

Mainly for ease and cheapness of construction, bridge trusses of moderate span are usually built with parallel chords rather than with a

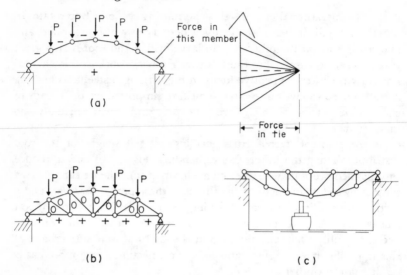

FIG. 4.2. Bowstring trusses.

curved upper chord. Since a straight chord cannot act as a linear arch, the web members in such trusses carry force whatever the loading. Various patterns of truss, some of them named after pioneer engineers of the early days of the railways, have been used: a few are shown in Fig. 4.3. The Pratt truss has the advantage that the longest web members, the diagonals, are almost always in tension while the shorter verticals are in compression. Since lower design stresses must be used in compression compared with tension, this saves some weight and cost. In the obsolete Howe truss, shown at (b), the reverse is the case: the diagonals are in compression and the verticals in tension. It was used in some of the early timber railway bridges, in which for ease of erection the verticals consisted of wrought-iron bars fitted with turnbuckles. The Warren truss, still very common, consists of a series of equilateral triangles, and has the practical advantage that all the members are of the same length (Fig. 4.3c).

Wide, deep rivers create construction problems which have been overcome by cantilever systems. The trussed cantilever bridge (Fig. 4.4d) has side spans which project or cantilever out beyond the pier on

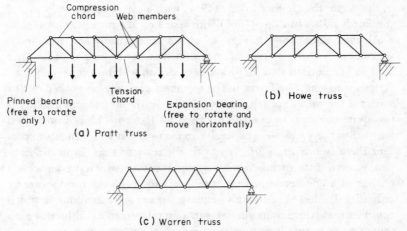

FIG. 4.3. Simply supported bridge trusses.

either bank. The gap in the middle is closed by a simply supported truss which can be lifted into position from a barge or built out as extensions of the cantilever spans to meet in mid-stream. In this case a temporary member is used on each side and later removed. The support arrangements for this kind of bridge are important: it must be securely located and yet be free to expand and contract horizontally with change in stress or temperature. One possible support system is shown in the figure. Except for suspension bridges, the largest spans yet achieved are

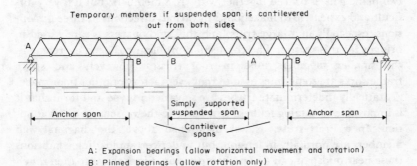

A: Expansion bearings (allow horizontal movement and rotation)
B: Pinned bearings (allow rotation only)

FIG. 4.4. Trussed cantilever bridge.

in this form: the Quebec bridge (1917) with a centre span of 549 m and the Forth railway bridge (1890) with spans of 521 m.

All the trusses shown in Figs. 4.1 to 4.3 are statically determinate, as we can easily check by the rule mentioned at the beginning of Chapter 3. It will be noticed that they have been drawn with hinges at the joints. Strictly speaking, the forces in the members can only be worked out by statics if the joints are frictionless hinges. In the nineteenth century it was quite common to construct trussed bridges with hinged or pinned joints. But the joints were expensive to make and it was difficult to prevent them from rusting up. It was finally realized that if this did happen, or even if the members were riveted together, which prevented any change of angle between them, the direct forces in the members were only slightly altered, although bending stresses were introduced which could increase the maximum stress in a member considerably. But even these do not normally reduce the strength of the structure, for reasons which we will look at later, and the practice of providing hinges was abandoned, though the engineer still assumes hinges when he analyses a truss.

All the trusses shown consist of a series of triangles. This is by far the most common, though not the only way of forming a plane trussed framework. The simplest framed structure in three dimensions, corresponding to the triangle in two dimensions, is the tetrahedron (Fig. 4.5a). The bridge truss shown at (b) consists of tetrahedra, and is a true space truss. Theoretically it should be more economical in material than the conventional arrangement, shown at (c), which is made up of two plane trusses braced together with cross members; but it is very difficult and expensive to make joints in various directions in three dimensions, especially in a large truss, and this kind of truss is rarely used in bridges for this reason. The connection problem has been overcome in the smaller members used in roof trusses, however, and space frameworks are sometimes used to roof over factory or other floor space.

Statically indeterminate trusses are so varied in type and form that it is impossible to catalogue them here, or give the reasons for their adoption. In a Pratt truss, as was mentioned above, the diagonal web members are normally in tension, but under certain loading conditions those near midspan can go into compression. Since they are then much weaker the middle panel is sometimes provided with two diagonals, as in

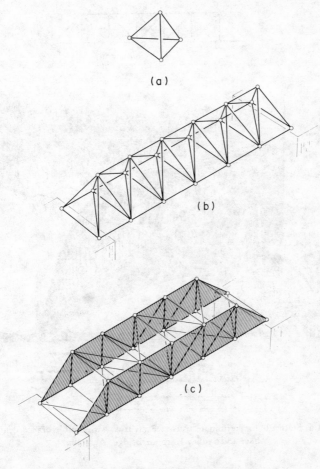

(a)

(b)

(c)

FIG. 4.5. Three-dimensional frameworks.

Fig. 4.6a, so that one will always be in tension. This makes the truss statically indeterminate internally. Trusses can also be redundant because of the conditions of support. For example, Sydney Harbour Bridge (Fig. 4.6b), a trussed two-hinged arch with a span of 504 m (one of the two largest structures of this type in the world) is statically indeterminate because a pinned support is not essential at both ends for

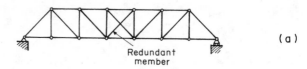

(a)

Redundant
member

—504 m—

(b)

FIG. 4.6. Statically indeterminate trusses: Pratt truss with double-braced central bay, and Sydney Harbour Bridge, Australia.

stability; a sliding support would be adequate at one end. If one member in such a two-hinged arch failed the arch would become three-hinged, and would still have enough members to make it a stable assemblage of bars. A second member near the one which failed might then, however, be so severely overstressed as to fail in its turn; the structure would then collapse. Likewise, if one abutment yielded to such an extent that it became for all practical purposes a sliding support, the arch would be converted to a simply supported curved truss, and in theory would still be stable. In this case failure would be total and immediate, however, even under the weight of the bridge alone, because it would not have been designed to act in this way. Statical indeterminacy, therefore, may not protect a structure from abrupt collapse when failure occurs in one part.

Beams

A beam supports loads by virtue of its ability to resist bending between supports. In this sense a truss like that shown in Fig. 4.3a is a beam, even though the forces in the individual members are direct (tensile or compressive) in nature. But the term "beam" is usually reserved for solid structures—timber joists, steel girders and so on—rather than for trusses.

Beams are easily the commonest of structural types. A fallen tree lying across a stream and the wooden joists under the floor and in the ceiling of one's house are beams. So are the channel-shaped steel members in the car chassis which support its weight between front and back axles, the wings of an aircraft, the hulls of boats and also their masts, the backs of chairs, and the frame of the ordinary bed. To the engineering student the behaviour of a simple beam and the distribution of stresses in it may seem very obvious. But it took several centuries of concentrated effort by the leading scientists of the time before the problem was solved. Leonardo da Vinci (1452-1519) found, probably by experiment, that the strength of a timber beam is proportional to the square of its depth: at least, one of the drawings in his notebooks seems to indicate this (Fig. 4.7). Galileo (1564-1642) confirmed this conclusion on the

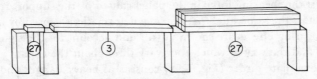

FIG. 4.7. Strength of timber beams (after Leonardo da Vinci).

basis of an assumption as to how the stresses in a beam vary from top to bottom. His assumption was quite in error, but because he was consistent in his mistake he was able to arrive at extremely important conclusions as to the limiting size of structures, as we saw in Chapter 2. Later investigators came nearer to the truth, but the problem of the stress distribution was not finally solved in a clear practical statement until 1773, by the brilliant French engineer and scientist, Coulomb (1736-1806). Even then, a rigorous mathematical proof did not appear for another 50 years.

The forces in the members of a simple truss give us an insight into bending action. Under a unit load placed centrally on the bottom chord of a Pratt truss with the layout shown in Fig. 4.8a, for example, the forces in the bars are as shown. In a Howe truss, in which the diagonals slope upwards towards the middle of the span, instead of downwards as in the Pratt truss, we find the forces shown at (b). We might reasonably expect that in a truss with double diagonals in each panel and with a load of two units at mid-span the member forces would be approximately the sum of those in (a) and (b), and this is the case (Fig. 4.8c), although since this structure is statically indeterminate the precise values of the forces depend on the relative stiffnesses of the members. The points to remark are that:

(i)   the forces in the top and bottom chord members in any one panel are equal, and they increase in proportion to the distance of the midpoint of the panel from the nearer support;

(ii) the forces in the diagonal members are equal and opposite in sign and have the same values in all panels.

In fact, the chord members have to resist the bending moment in the truss, which under this loading equals the support reaction times the distance to the panel in question, whereas the diagonal members have to resist the shearing force in the panel caused by the support reaction, and this is the same in all panels. The deformations caused by bending and shearing effects are shown at (d), and account for the signs of the forces and the way in which they vary throughout the truss.

A steel plate girder (Fig. 4.9a) consists of heavy flanges and a thin web welded together. The web is usually strengthened by a number of vertical stiffeners spaced so as to divide it into roughly square panels. If such a girder is loaded with a central load, the forces in it are very similar to those in the truss of Fig. 4.8c, except that in the web the force is naturally diffused somewhat. Still, the directions of the tensile and compressive stresses in each panel are clearly the same. As the load is in-

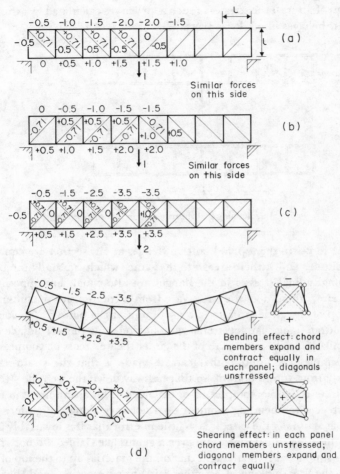

FIG. 4.8. Bending and shearing action in a simply supported truss.

creased, the web panels start to buckle under the action of the inclined compressive stresses, which more or less disappear, leaving what is known as a tension field in each panel (Fig. 4.9b), the buckled part of the web carrying a tensile force, much as in the Pratt truss of Fig. 4.8a, and each stiffener a compressive force to balance this. Indeed, in the preliminary design of aircraft the stresses in such a girder are calculated by assuming that it behaves like a Pratt truss.

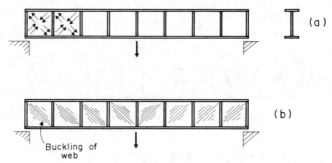

FIG. 4.9. Bending and shearing action in a plate girder.

The forces in the top and bottom flanges at any section are equal in magnitude, and if their areas are the same (which is usually the case) the longitudinal stresses in the flanges are also equal, but opposite in sign. How, then, does the stress vary from a compressive maximum at the top of the girder to a tensile maximum at the bottom? Obviously, the bottom flange cannot stretch without stretching the web adjacent to it; similarly, in the upper half of the girder the web must be compressed. The simplest assumption that can be made is that the strain varies linearly from top to bottom, so that halfway down the web the steel in the girder is neither compressed or extended. This assumption, in fact, is correct if the bending moment does not vary along the girder; if it does, as is usually the case, it is so little in error that it is invariably used in engineering calculations. But even a genius like Galileo did not arrive at this simple truth: he thought that all the material up to the top of the beam (he was thinking of a timber joist) was in tension, and that the compressive force was somehow concentrated right at the top.

We can see what happens if we take a thick rubber beam with a square pattern of lines marked on it, and bend it (Fig. 4.10). The vertical lines remain straight, and it is obvious that the squares in the upper half compress in proportion to their distance from mid-depth, and that those in the lower half extend in the same way. The horizontal plane halfway down the beam at which level the longitudinal stress is zero is

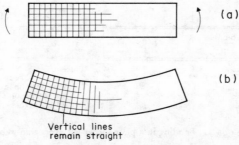

FIG. 4.10. Bending in a rubber beam.

called the neutral plane. Once the assumption is taken as to how the longitudinal strain varies, the rest of the solution is relatively plain sailing, provided the material is linear-elastic (that is, so long as stress is proportional to strain). In this case, the longitudinal *stress* is also proportional to the distance above or below the neutral plane. In a flanged girder with a very thin web and thick flanges, we can assume that the stress in the web makes so little contribution to the bending resistance of the beam that we can ignore it. Also, the stress in the flange at any particular section can be taken as uniform (it is very nearly so if the flange is not too thick and wide). Now, looking at the left-hand half of the beam (Fig. 4.11), the reaction $W/2$ at the left-hand end tends to rotate it about the point 0 at mid-span, and this is balanced by the resisting moments of the two flange forces, which are equal to $A\sigma/2$, where $A/2$ is the cross-sectional area of each flange. The turning moment of the weight is $M = W/2 \cdot 1/2 = W1/4$, and the resisting moment of the flanges is $A\sigma/2 \cdot d/2 + A\sigma/2 \cdot d/2 = A\sigma d/2$. Putting these equal to each other, we have

$$M = \frac{A\sigma d}{2}$$

$$\text{or } \sigma = \frac{2M}{Ad}$$

In a joist with a rectangular cross-section, half of the material carries less than half the maximum possible stress at the section, which is obviously wasteful of material. In fact, it turns out that for a beam of this cross-section, with the same cross-sectional area A and depth d, the

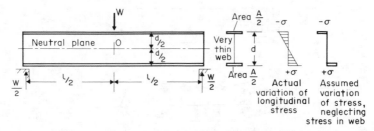

FIG. 4.11. Bending in a plate girder with very thin web.

maximum stress is $6M/Ad$, which is three times as great as in the girder. This is the penalty for not arranging the material to the best advantage, that is, as far as possible from the neutral plane. We may also note that for such a joist the bending moment that can be carried is equal to $Ad\,\sigma/6M$ *or* $bd^2\sigma/6$. Thus for a beam of a given width b and of rectangular cross-section the flexural strength is proportional to the *square* of the depth.

In general, the maximum stress σ in a beam of symmetrical cross-section due to a bending moment M is given by the expression $\sigma = M/I \cdot d/2$, in which I is the property of the cross-section of the beam known as the second moment of area. For the ideal flanged girder we have been discussing, I is equal to $Ad^2/4$, while for the rectangular section it is $Ad^2/12$. The more the material is concentrated near the top and bottom of the beam, the greater the value of I and, consequently, the smaller the maximum stress.

Light roof beams made of two "flanges" of reinforcing steel bar or steel channel section joined together by a web of steel rod (Fig. 4.12a) come very close to the ideal, but solid flanged girders are much more common. The earliest, in cast iron, had very large tension flanges because of the weakness of the material in tension (Fig. 4.12b). Until recently, mild steel girders produced by rolling white-hot steel billets had slightly sloping flanges, but improved rolling processes now make it possible to form a section whose shape is closer to the ideal (Fig. 2.10a), and up to about 1 m deep. Larger steel girders (up to about 4 m deep) can be made from plates or structural sections by welding or by riveting (a process now obsolete) or high-tensile steel bolting.

Another way of getting close to the ideal can be seen in the sandwich

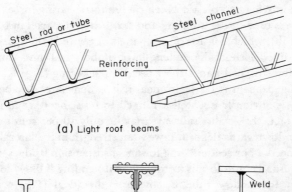

(a) Light roof beams

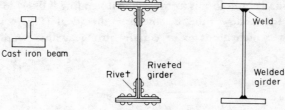

(b) Joist and girder sections

FIG. 4.12. Beams of various sections.

panel originally developed for the aircraft industry (Fig. 4.13a). Two sheets of aluminium alloy, which provide the bending resistance, are

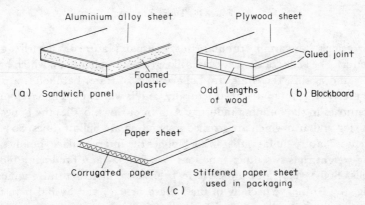

(a) Sandwich panel

(b) Blockboard

(c)

FIG. 4.13. Panel construction.

separated by foamed plastic which carries the shearing force. The same principle is used in the building and furniture industries in blockboard (Fig. 4.13b), which consists of two panels of plywood the space between which is filled with small odd lengths of timber; and, on a smaller scale still, in the stiffened paper sheet used in packaging (Fig. 4.13c).

A flanged beam is far from ideal if it is bent laterally, because the material is obviously not well arranged to resist bending in this direction: in fact, the *I* value sideways may be only 10 per cent or so of the value for downwards flexure. If we want strength in the lateral direction also we need a box section—the towers of suspension bridges, for example, are usually built in this form—while if bending is likely to be in *any* direction the hollow tube is obviously the ideal (Fig. 4.14). Steel scaffolding, which needs to be equally strong against bending in all

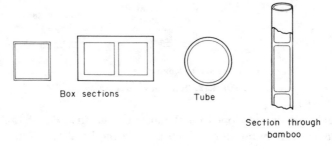

Box sections   Tube

Section through
bamboo

FIG. 4.14. Tubular beams.

directions, is invariably tubular. But, as usual, Nature did it earlier and better. The stalks of slender plants like grasses and bamboo, which have to stand against the wind, are hollow tubes of fibre; bamboo is a particularly efficient material structurally, and is widely used in developing countries in the building industry. And in our own bodies the bones of the leg and arm which are stressed in bending are hollow tubes. So efficient is Nature, in fact, that in such bones the interior space, beside saving weight, has two other functions—storing fat and producing blood cells. Some very large tubes have been used in structural engineering—by Brunel, especially in the Saltash bridge, and by Baker in the Forth railway bridge—but the biggest of all are now in service in the columns of the huge oil-production platforms in the North Sea.

Another way of increasing bending resistance is by a change of shape which deepens the section. If we take a sheet of foolscap writing paper and try to support it on two pencils at its ends, we know almost without attempting it that it will bend and slip down between the pencils (Fig. 4.15a). But if it is folded into a series of longitudinal corrugations, it

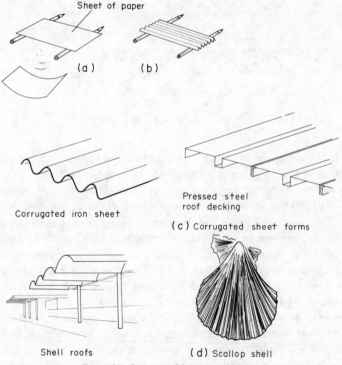

Sheet of paper

(a)   (b)

Corrugated iron sheet

Pressed steel
roof decking

(c) Corrugated sheet forms

Shell roofs   (d) Scallop shell

FIG. 4.15. Corrugated beams and plates.

supports itself quite easily, and will even carry a weight much heavier than itself. The reason is simply that the corrugations greatly increase the depth of the paper as a beam, and so reduce the stresses and, consequently, the deflection which is the direct cause of its slipping between the supports. The principle can be seen at (c) in corrugated iron and asbestos cement roof sheeting, on a much larger scale in the thin reinforced concrete shell roofs used for factory construction, and in nature in the shells of molluscs like the scallop. Another way of economizing in material can be seen in the castellated steel beam (Fig. 4.16). A steel

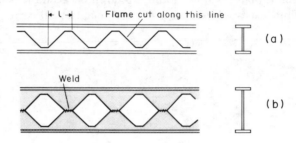

FIG. 4.16. Castellated joist.

joist is cut along the web with a cutting torch as shown at (a); the lower half is then moved along and rewelded to the upper half, as at (b). This increases the depth of the beam and therefore its bending strength, and removes material from the web, where it is relatively ineffective.

In the castellated beam the designer must be sure that the *shearing* stresses do not become too great. We must now look briefly at the question of shear. As we saw a little earlier, the bending moment which a timber joist of rectangular section can carry at a maximum stress σ is $bd^2\sigma/6$, where b is its width and d its depth (Fig. 4.17a). If such a beam is cut into two beams each of depth $d/2$, each one can carry a bending moment of $b(d/2)^2\sigma/6$ or $bd^2\sigma/24$, at the same maximum stress, so that if one is laid over the other and both are loaded the combined bending resistance is $bd^2\sigma/12$, or only half of that of the uncut beam. Each half acts as a beam on its own, and under the same load the deflection is four times, and the stress double, that in the uncut beam. The lower fibres of the upper half stretch and the upper fibres of the bottom half contract, so that sliding takes place between the upper and lower halves at their common surface.

It is obvious that in the uncut beam there must be stresses which act along the neutral plane to prevent this movement (Fig. 4.17c) and force the beam to act as a unit. Evidently, if a slice were cut off above the neutral surface shearing stresses would still be required to maintain

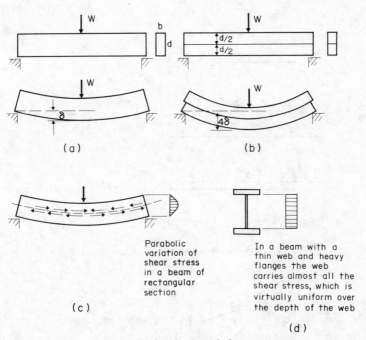

Parabolic
variation of
shear stress
in a beam of
rectangular
section

In a beam with a
thin web and heavy
flanges the web
carries almost all the
shear stress, which is
virtually uniform over
the depth of the web

(c)

(d)

Fig. 4.17. Shearing stress in beams.

unity of action, but they would be smaller. The shearing stresses must therefore diminish towards the top and bottom of the beam, and in fact for a rectangular beam the variation is parabolic. In a steel joist with a very thin web, the shearing stress is practically constant throughout the depth of the web (Fig. 4.17d). As we will see later, these stresses are equivalent to the diagonal tensile and compressive stresses shown in Fig. 4.9a.

The simplest case of bending is that of the beam with a central load which we have been discussing. The bending moment caused by the reaction at the left-hand support is equal to $W/2$ times x, the distance from the reaction to the point under consideration. Similarly, the bending moment increases from the right-hand support in the same way. We can draw a diagram to represent the variation of the bending moment along the beam (Fig. 4.18a). If the loading is distributed uniformly

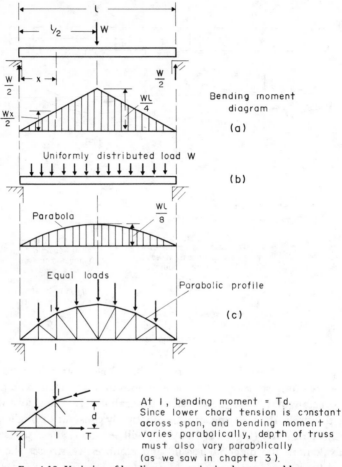

Bending moment
diagram

(a)

Uniformly distributed load W

(b)

Parabola

$\frac{WL}{8}$

Equal loads

Parabolic profile

(c)

At I, bending moment = Td.
Since lower chord tension is constant
across span, and bending moment
varies parabolically, depth of truss
must also vary parabolically
(as we saw in chapter 3).

FIG. 4.18. Variation of bending moment in simply supported beams.

along the beam, instead of being concentrated at the mid-point, the variation of bending moment is parabolic with a central (maximum) value of $W1/8$, or half that when the same load is concentrated at midspan (Fig. 4.18b).

It will be remembered that a bowstring truss with a parabolically curved upper chord carries a uniformly distributed load by a direct thrust in this chord and a uniform tension in the horizontal bottom chord. We can now see why this must be so from a different point of view. At any cross-section such as 1-1 (Fig. 4.18c) the bending moment in the truss, considering it as a beam, is resisted by the force T in the bottom chord multiplied by the depth of the truss, so that the depth of the truss varies in the same way as the bending moment, that is, parabolically.

Let us look at one more example of bending moments, that of a cantilever bridge (Fig. 4.19a) carrying a uniformly distributed load over its

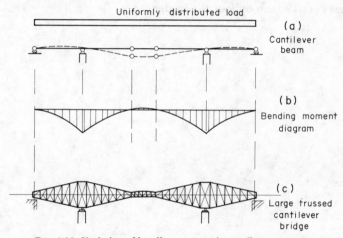

Uniformly distributed load

(a)
Cantilever beam

(b)
Bending moment diagram

(c)
Large trussed cantilever bridge

FIG. 4.19. Variation of bending moment in cantilever systems.

whole length. The bridge consists of a central simply supported span, for which the diagram of bending moment variation is similar to that just discussed. It is flanked by two sections which can each be looked upon as two cantilevers poised on a pier. The bending moment diagram for each will be two triangles which are curved because of the distributed load on them. Bearing in mind that we draw these diagrams downwards because these sections of the bridge curve downwards, the complete diagram will be as shown in Fig. 4.19b.

Comparing this diagram with the shape of a large trussed cantilever bridge like the Quebec railway bridge (Fig. 4.19c) we must be struck with the very strong resemblance between the two. In very large bridges the weight of the structure itself is easily the most important load which it has to support. Assuming as a rough approximation that the weight is uniformly distributed along the length of the bridge, it will be evident from our discussion on the bowstring truss that for maximum economy of material the depth of the framework should everywhere be roughly proportional to the depth of the bending moment diagram for a uniformly distributed load. If this is done, the diagonal web members are relatively free from stress when the bridge is carrying only its own weight and the forces in the bottom and top chords are equal, and more or less constant throughout the bridge.

CHAPTER 5

Collapse

WE HAVE already seen how a simple statically indeterminate pin-jointed structure like the three-bar frame of Fig. 3.3 collapses under load following the development of a plastic state in enough bars to turn it into a mechanism. In this chapter we will find that failure by the formation of a mechanism is a general structural phenomenon.

In our earlier discussion we noted that:

1. At the point of collapse the load can be calculated from statics, from a knowledge of the strength of the parts which fail.

2. If the stresses in the structure in the elastic range are not uniform throughout the different parts, the structure will usually carry more load before it fails than would be given by simply scaling up the load and the maximum stress caused by it to the point where the latter reaches the ultimate strength of the material. Design on the basis of elastic stresses may thus give too conservative an estimate of the ultimate strength of the structure, and hence of the margin of strength beyond the working load.

3. There will be no such additional reserve of strength if the structure is designed so that under elastic conditions it is uniformly stressed in the different parts, or if it is statically determinate. Nor will there be the expected reserve of strength unless the material is ductile enough to enable the parts which become plastic before failure to continue deforming at constant force until the mechanism has developed.

4. Failure by the formation of a mechanism occurs in statically determinate as well as in statically indeterminate (or redundant) structures, but in the former no warning is given of the onset of collapse such as is afforded by an increased rate of deformation when one part of a redundant structure becomes plastic.

In structures of ductile material, a mechanism forms when plasticity has developed at a sufficient number of points. When the material is brittle, a mechanism will still develop because of local failure by cracking at enough places. We saw how this happens in a stone voussoir arch in Chapter 3 (Fig. 3.29 and the accompanying discussion). The earliest recorded calculation of structural strength, in fact, was a collapse analysis of a brittle structure, the dome of St. Peter's Cathedral in Rome. Cracks had appeared, and the question was how strong the wrought-iron chains encircling the base of the dome should be to prevent collapse. In the report by Poleni in 1748 it was assumed that the dome would split vertically into a number of "orange-slice" segments (Fig. 5.1a), a mode of failure of domes that had already been suggested by Leonardo da Vinci. Each slice, together with a slice of the drum below it, would pivot about the base of the drum, with hinges at points A, B, and C (Fig. 5.1b).

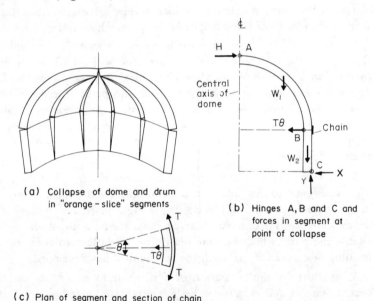

(a) Collapse of dome and drum in "orange–slice" segments

(b) Hinges A, B and C and forces in segment at point of collapse

(c) Plan of segment and section of chain showing resultant force $T\theta$ acting inwards

FIG. 5.1. Collapse analysis of dome of St. Peter's Cathedral, Rome.

If T is the tension in the chains, and each drum segment subtends a small angle θ at the centre of the drum (Fig. 5.1c), the resultant force exerted by the chains acts towards the centre and is equal to $T\theta$. At the point of collapse the forces on the segments of dome and drum are as shown at (b): the weights W_1 and W_2 of the segments acting vertically downwards, the force $T\theta$, the outward thrust H at the apex of the dome, and the reaction components X and Y at the base of the drum. We can solve the problem by first considering the equilibrium of the dome segment and taking moments of the forces H and W_1 about B, which gives us the value of H, and then looking at the equilibrium of the complete combination of dome and wall segments and chains, and taking moments about C of the forces H, W_1, W_2, and $T\theta$. This immediately gives us the value of T which is required to maintain stability, and hence enables the chains to be designed.

This analysis, a remarkable feat for its time, went straight to the core of the problem of how to prevent failure of the dome. Fig. 5.2, taken from Poleni's report, shows that the three mathematicians who were entrusted with the calculations also made use of the recently discovered funicular method (Chapter 3) to determine whether the line of thrust in the dome remained within it everywhere. It is worth noting that the problem of calculating the *elastic* stresses in the dome before it cracked is much more difficult, and a solution would have been quite impossible at that time. The analysis was not, however, accepted without criticism. "If it was possible", observed one architect, "to build this great dome without mathematics, it should be possible to repair it without mathematics." Suspicion among practical men of the work of theoreticians is a recurring theme in structural history. Tredgold, one of the founders of the Institution of Civil Engineers in the early part of the nineteenth century, remarked cynically that "the stability of a structure is in inverse ratio to the science of its builder"; and this attitude is still not unknown, which is a pity, for the best engineering solutions usually stem from a judicious blend of practical experience and theory.

From 1800 onwards great advances were made in the science of stress analysis, and by the end of the century it was possible to calculate stresses in the more common kinds of structure with reasonable accuracy so long as the material remained linear-elastic. As was only to be expected, designers concentrated their attention mainly on the stresses

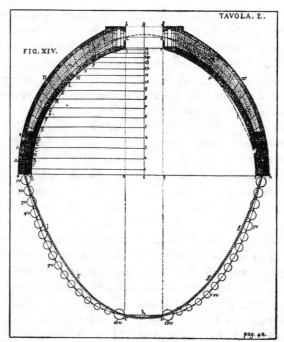

FIG. 5.2. Poleni's analysis of funicular forces in dome of St. Peter's.

in structures under the working loads, with the aim of ensuring that they were well below the elastic limit of the material. Interest in the direct approach to the ultimate strength of structures initiated by Poleni and others declined. In any case, the most popular structural types in the nineteenth century were statically determinate. As we have seen, for such structures the approach to design is the same, whether we work on the basis of elastic stresses or collapse.

Modern interest in the collapse of structures began in Germany about 60 years ago, but by 1939 little progress had been made and the only research of any magnitude in progress was at Cambridge in England. During the Second World War, unhappily, there was plenty of opportunity to study the behaviour of steel and reinforced concrete framed structures under unusually heavy loads like blast and falling masonry, and this provided full-scale confirmation of the ideas which were being developed on the collapse of structures of ductile material. Many older people can still remember taking refuge in their homes under a heavy steel table, the Morrison Shelter, during air raids. This shelter was designed on collapse principles to carry the debris when the house collapsed on it.

Since 1945 great progress has been made in the study of modes of collapse of different types of structure, and it is now possible very generally to predict collapse and to design on the basis of collapse. Much of the work has been done on steel beams and frames. First let us consider, therefore, the behaviour of a simply supported mild-steel flanged girder bridge (Fig. 5.3a). Mild steel which is free from the effects of cold work and overstrain has—as we saw in Chapter 2—a very unusual stress-strain curve, shown again at (b): the linear-elastic range of behaviour OA, in both tension and compression, is followed by a purely plastic range AB during which the steel extends or shortens freely at constant stress. The material later picks up further strength before it fails, but it is this plastic range which particularly concerns us here.

To make things simple let us assume that the girder can be treated in the idealized way discussed earlier (see Fig. 4.11) in which the two flanges carry the whole of the bending moment at any section and the stress in them is the maximum in the girder at that section. If the bridge carries a uniformly distributed load the greatest bending moment is at the centre of the span. If the load is gradually increased there comes a point at which the stress in the two flanges at midspan reaches the yield stress σ_y. At this stage, without any further increase in the load, the top flange suddenly shortens plastically at this section by up to ten to twenty times the elastic strain just before it yielded, and the bottom flange extends similarly. The girder develops what is known as a *plastic hinge*, and sinks downwards at midspan (Fig. 5.3c). The bending moment at which this happens is very easily calculated: it is simply the force in either flange $(A/2 \cdot \sigma_y)$ multiplied by the depth d of the girder, that is $A/2 \cdot d\sigma_y$ (Fig. 5.3d). The plastic deformation ceases when the end of the plastic range B is reached, but most of the deformation at midspan will remain if the load is removed, because the material follows the path BC if the stress is removed, not back along the route BAO. The bridge has a kink in it, and has for all practical purposes failed. A plastic hinge should not be thought of as a smooth pinned connection between the

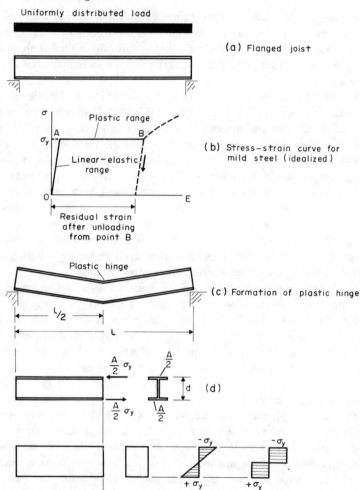

Uniformly distributed load

(a) Flanged joist

(b) Stress–strain curve for mild steel (idealized)

(c) Formation of plastic hinge

(d)

(e) Stresses in beam of rectangular section:
(i) When yield has just started;
(ii) When central section is completely plastic

FIG. 5.3. Plastic behaviour of mild-steel flanged girder.

two halves of the beam. It takes a considerable bending moment—called the plastic moment—to overcome the bending resistance of the girder section, and for the hinge to bend to the limit of the plastic range the plastic moment must be maintained. It is better to think of it as a *rusty* hinge whose frictional resistance has to be overcome to start it turning, and to keep it turning.

If the beam were of rectangular section it would still develop a plastic hinge; in this case all the material in the upper half of the beam becomes plastic in compression, and all the lower half plastic in tension (Fig. 5.3e). The hinge does not appear so suddenly as in the idealized flanged girder, however, because when the material at the top and bottom of the beam just reaches the yield point the more lightly stressed material in the interior has still some way to go before yielding.

When the steel in the beam has only a small plastic range, or none at all—as is the case in mild steel which has been cold-worked, or in one of the higher-yield structural steels—a sharply defined plastic hinge cannot normally be expected. Instead, at a section where the bending moment is high enough a rather more widespread zone of yielded material develops, but it will still behave as a plastic hinge from the point of view of the structure as a whole.

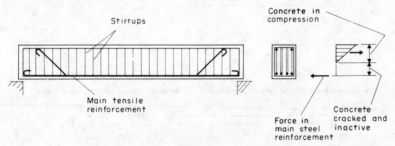

FIG. 5.4. Reinforced concrete beam.

In a reinforced concrete beam, steel bars embedded in the side which is in tension (the underside in a simply supported beam carrying downwards loads) provide the tensile strength which the concrete alone does not possess (Fig. 5.4). These bars are usually assembled in a cage of reinforcement together with thin bent bars called stirrups whose main job is to help to resist the shearing force, and all are wired securely together so that they are kept in position when the concrete is placed around them.

When such a beam is loaded, the concrete soon cracks below the neutral plane, especially near midspan, and becomes inoperative except as a means of connecting the tensile reinforcement to the concrete above the neutral plane, which is in compression. Beyond this stage the tensile force in the steel and the compressive force in the concrete act together to provide the resistance to bending. In most beams the amount of tensile reinforcement is such that it yields and stretches plastically before the concrete fails, and a kind of hinge thus develops at midspan.

If the material of the beam is plain concrete, stone masonry, or even a steel which for some reason is brittle, hinges can still develop, but because little or no tensile strength can be depended upon they offer no bending resistance to rotation, and may be called *brittle* hinges. Fatal as such a hinge is in a simply supported beam, it is perfectly normal in a masonry arch or buttress as it degenerates towards collapse, as Fig. 3.29 showed.

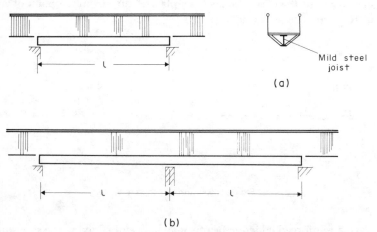

(a)

Mild steel joist

(b)

Fig. 5.5. Single-span and two-span steel joist bridges.

Now let us consider the two steel girder foot-bridges shown in Fig. 5.5, and see how collapse occurs by the formation of plastic hinges. The bridges each have one girder of mild steel, with the same cross-section, which behaves in the idealized way we discussed earlier. The bridges carry a uniformly distributed loading w per unit length (which includes their own weight).

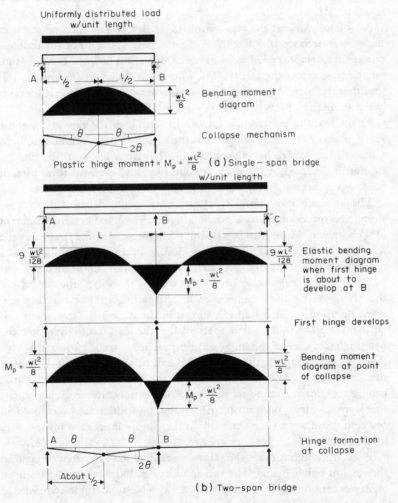

FIG. 5.6. Plastic behaviour of single-span and two-span joist bridges.

The single span bridge (Fig. 5.6a) remains elastic until the bending moment $wl^2/8$ in the centre of the span reaches the plastic moment of resistance Mp of the girder. A plastic hinge then forms at midspan, pronounced central deflection occurs, and the beam has effectively failed. Since $M_p = wl^2/8$, the load w per unit length at which this occurs is equal to $8M_p/1^2$.

Now let us look at the two-span bridge. Before any yielding starts in the steel it behaves in a linear-elastic manner, and a statically indeterminate analysis will need to be carried out to find how the bending moment varies across the girder. The solution is shown at (b) and we will find that the bending moment is greatest over the pier, where it is exactly the same ($wl^2/8$) as in the single-span bridge.

As the loading increases, a hinge will form over the pier at the same value of w as in the first bridge. But the structure has not failed: in fact, although the bridge becomes more flexible from here on, the change cannot be detected by the ordinary observer, and even the formation of the hinge will be scarcely noticeable except on expert inspection.

The bridge is now statically determinate, and consists of two simply supported spans joined by a plastic hinge at which the bending moment (M_p) is known. More load can be put on before one of the spans, say the left-hand one, develops a hinge very close to midspan and collapses as a mechanism (theoretically, both spans should do this simultaneously, but in real life one will always be slightly weaker than the other or have a slightly larger bending moment in it, and fail first). The bending moment distribution at collapse is shown in the diagram. Now when collapse takes place in the single span bridge, the load has to overcome the bending resistance of the hinge at midspan only; in the two-span bridge there is also a hinge at the pier, and it can be seen from Fig. 5.6b that this one turns through half the angle of the one at midspan as collapse progresses. For the same increment of deflection after collapse starts, therefore, the load per unit length on the span which fails has to do 50 per cent more work than the load on the simply supported bridge, and must therefore be 50 per cent greater; that is, it has a value of $12M_p/1^2$.

Thus, although it takes the same intensity of load to produce yield in the steel in either bridge, the two-span bridge has a reserve of strength of 50 per cent beyond the limit of elasticity which the single-span bridge does not possess. Until recently, as we have seen, it has been the general practice to design structures so that the maximum stress is limited to some fraction of the yield stress (or the stress at the elastic limit where there is no clear yield point). If these two structures were proportioned on this principle, they would have the same cross-sections since the maximum stress in each is the same so long as all the material remains elastic throughout; but the two-span bridge would carry 1½ times as much load per unit length as the single-span one before it collapsed, and would thus be unnecessarily strong. Design on the basis of collapse is more rational and economical in this case; for the same collapse load w the two-span bridge would have a lighter girder.

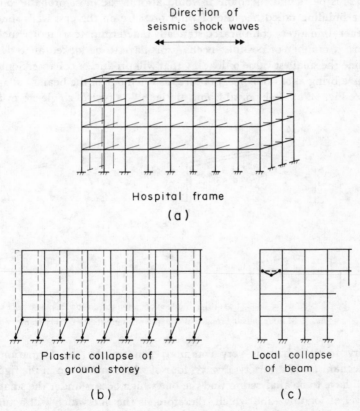

Direction of
seismic shock waves

Hospital frame

(a)

Plastic collapse of
ground storey

(b)

Local collapse
of beam

(c)

FIG. 5.7. Plastic collapse of four-storey reinforced concrete frame building.

That a large structure really can fail by the formation of a mechanism was brought home to the author a few years ago, during a visit to a small Turkish town which had just suffered an earthquake. The building was a new four-storey hospital with a reinforced concrete skeleton frame (Fig. 5.7). The structure had been shaken so severely backwards and forwards in a longitudinal direction that the columns had cracked at the top and bottom of the ground storey and developed plastic hinges (Fig. 5.7b). During the earthquake the whole structure above the hinges had swayed backwards and forwards, and was left with a permanent deflection of about 40 mm.

This particular mechanism would also be the most probable one if the building failed because of wind pressure on the end walls; but in general, in a very complicated statically indeterminate structure such as this, a number of possible mechanisms have to be looked at to determine the smallest value of loading that will produce a collapse. Some of these bring about only local failure, as when one of the beams collapses (see Fig. 5.7c). The portal frame of Fig. 5.8, a type of single-storey fac-

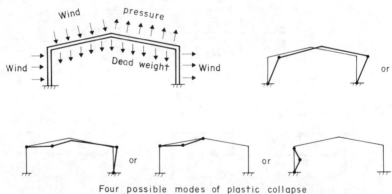

Four possible modes of plastic collapse

FIG. 5.8. Four possible modes of collapse of single-storey factory frame.

tory frame which is very common, can fail by the formation of mechanisms in a variety of ways, four of which are shown in the figure. All have to be analysed to find the one which occurs under the smallest level of loading (and which, therefore, is the one which will actually develop); but since the analyses are based on statics, they are relatively

simple—much easier than the analysis of the frame as a linear-elastic
fixed arch, and infinitely simpler than analysis once the material has
yielded anywhere.

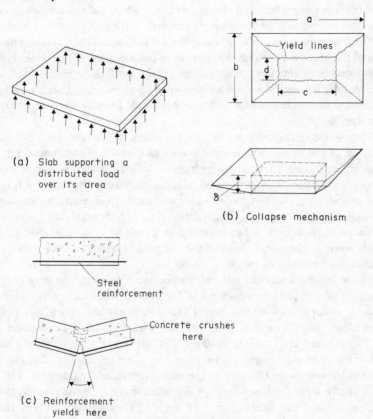

(a) Slab supporting a
distributed load
over its area

(b) Collapse mechanism

Steel
reinforcement

Concrete crushes
here

(c) Reinforcement
yields here

FIG. 5.9. Collapse of simply supported reinforced concrete slab.

The main difficulty in collapse analysis arises from uncertainty as to
where the hinges form and the geometry of the resulting mechanism.
This is especially so when collapse is three-dimensional, as it must be,
for example, in flat plates. In a rectangular slab supported around the
perimeter and carrying a uniformly distributed downward load over the

whole area (to take a very simple case) failure occurs by cracking in the pattern shown in Fig. 5.9b. Along the lines of cracking, which are called *yield lines,* the full moment of resistance of the slab per unit length of the crack is generated, and this resists the tendency of the load to force the central portion of the slab downwards. Once collapse has begun there is a geometrical relation between the additional central deflection δ and the angle θ by which the slab opens out along each yield line (Fig. 5.9c) and once this has been determined the work done by the load in descending through the distance δ is equated to the work that has to be expended in opening out the slab along the yield lines by the corresponding angles.

This will give the intensity of load necessary to produce the assumed pattern of yield lines, but if the dimensions c and d of the central portion of the slab are varied, a lower intensity of load than this may suffice to cause collapse. The pattern of failure which actually occurs will be the one which gives the smallest load, and usually this pattern can only be found by trial and error. An additional complication is that since the reinforcement in such a slab usually runs parallel to the sides, and may be different in the two directions, the moment of resistance along a yield line varies with its direction.

In less simple cases the geometry of collapse can become very complicated, as the yield line patterns in Figs. 5.10a and b indicate. Nevertheless, collapse analysis is still very much simpler than elastic analysis, which can only be performed in practice with the aid of a computer.

The modern approach to collapse analysis has thrown new light on the stability of the masonry construction of the mediaeval and ancient worlds. As we saw in Chapter 3, French analysts, led by Danisy in 1732 (Fig. 3.28), were the first to realize that a masonry arch collapses by the formation of a mechanism, and to use trial thrust lines to verify the stability of an arch and to find the load required to bring about collapse. What they saw intuitively—that if a thrust line could be drawn which remained inside the thickness of the arch everywhere, it must be stable—has since been proved to be necessarily true. The thrust line drawn need not even be the actual one: indeed, in an arch consisting of masonry voussoirs with dry or weak mortar joints, there can be no certainty as to the precise location of the thrust line until the point of collapse is reached. From the time the centering which supports the

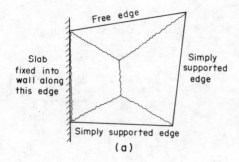

(a)

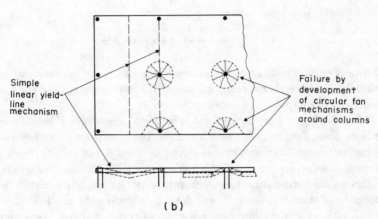

(b)

FIG. 5.10. Collapse patterns in slabs.

stonework during construction is removed, slight variations in the fit of the voussoirs and the smallest of movements in the abutments are enough to convert the arch into a three-hinged statically determinate structure (Fig. 5.11). But this in no way impairs its stability or its load-carrying capacity. In fact, provided the movements which occur are not so great as to change the geometry of the structure appreciably—which would require, in very general terms, movements of the order of at least 1 per cent of the span—then, as Heyman puts it, in referring to flying buttresses, "if on striking the centering, that buttress stands for 5 minutes, then it will stand for 500 years". Small foundation movements

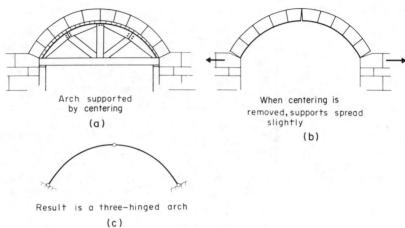

Arch supported
by centering
(a)

When centering is
removed, supports spread
slightly
(b)

Result is a three-hinged arch
(c)

FIG. 5.11. Settlement of a masonry arch.

naturally cause cracking of the masonry but this is the normal state of masonry, and merely expresses its inability to carry tension, not the imminence of collapse.

The drawing of trial thrust lines, which is a very simple if sometimes tedious operation, helps us to understand the behaviour of arches and flying buttresses. To take a simple example, a weightless arch carrying a vertical load at the crown (Fig. 5.12a), if the lines AB and AC joining points on the extrados at crown and springing lie completely within the thickness of the arch, the arch will not fail however great the load (provided, of course, the stone does not crush) because a thrust line which meets the requirements of stability can obviously be drawn. Again, although a flat arch or *plate-bande* between unyielding supports (Fig. 5.12b) may look unsafe, it cannot collapse as a mechanism under its own weight or additional downward loads, provided it fits tightly between the supports at either end and cannot simply slide down between them, because any number of thrust lines can be drawn which lie inside the stonework. If its thickness is very small compared with its span, however, it could fail by "snap-through" buckling (see Chapter 7).

A flying buttress, which transmits the thrust of a Gothic nave vault through an outer vertical buttress to the ground (Fig. 5.13c) is somewhat similar in action to a *plate-bande*. The centering to the but-

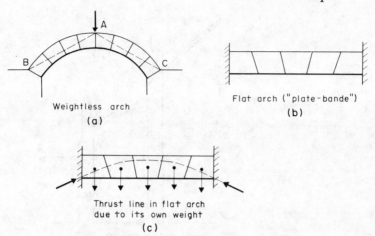

FIG. 5.12. Thrust lines in curved and flat arches.

tresses on either side of the nave would be struck (i.e. removed) before that of the nave vault, and at this stage each buttress would support merely its own weight. Assuming that it becomes a three-hinged arch on removal of its centering, the thrust line 1 will apply; under this condition the lateral thrust on the sides is at a minimum, since any other line drawn within the buttress would be flatter and would therefore correspond to a larger lateral thrust.

When the nave centering is struck, the full nave thrust, far greater in a typical Gothic cathedral than that due to the weight of the buttress itself, has to be transmitted through it. The thrust line flattens out, and the limit of the capacity of the flying buttress is reached when the line 2 applies. It is now a three-hinged arch in the opposite sense, and is about to collapse *upwards*. This is apparently what happened in the failure during construction of Amiens Cathedral, the reason being that the flying buttresses were not flat enough on top.

To the layman there must seem a danger that voussoir blocks could drop or be pushed out of a flat arch or buttress, but this is very unlikely to happen if it is properly designed. The frictional resistance between adjoining stones must first be overcome, and since the coefficient of friction between stone surfaces, with or without weak mortar, is 0.60 or more, this means that the thrust line must be inclined at an angle θ of

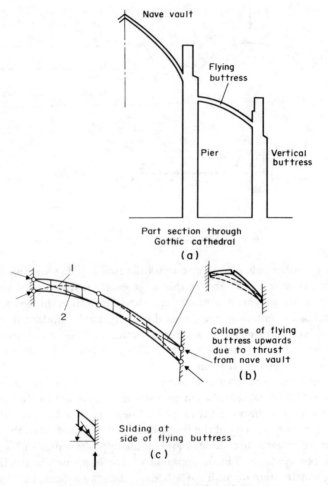

Nave vault

Flying
buttress

Pier

Vertical
buttress

Part section through
Gothic cathedral
(a)

1

2

Collapse of flying
buttress upwards
due to thrust
from nave vault
(b)

Sliding at
side of flying buttress
(c)

Fig. 5.13. Thrust lines in Gothic flying buttresses.

more than about 30° to the normal to the joint (Fig. 5.13c). One point
where this might happen is at the side of a flying buttress in the passive
condition of thrust, before the nave thrust has to be resisted. Gothic
builders may have had trouble at this point, and it could explain why
the voussoirs here are often supported by columns underneath.

Figure 5.14a shows a simplified section through the nave and side aisles of a Gothic cathedral which indicates how the flying buttresses support the nave vault (sometimes there are two buttresses, one above the other, the upper one being meant to take the thrust caused by the

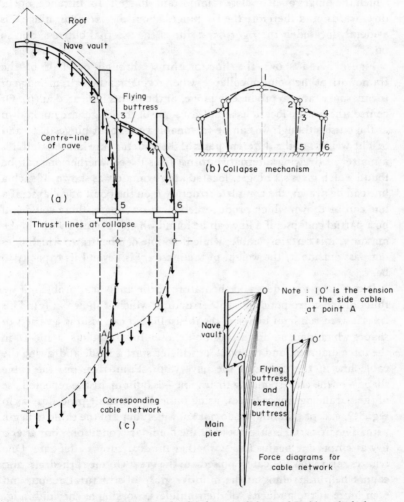

FIG. 5.14. Possible collapse mechanism in stone skeleton of Gothic cathedral.

weight of the roof and the wind on it). The idealized stone skeleton framework, consisting of nave vault rib, column, flying buttress, and external vertical buttress, is shown at (b), where a possible mechanism of collapse, containing eleven hinges, is also indicated. The way in which the hinges open or close is important: hinge 1, for instance, opens downwards, and therefore the rib hinges about the *extrados*; hinge 6 is evidently located at the *right-hand* side of the external buttress; and so on.

Figure 5.14a shows the line of thrust through one-half of the framework at the point of collapse, when it touches the extreme edge of the masonry, and so produces a hinge, at the points indicated at (b). Of course, the precise locations of at least some of the hinges are not known at the outset, though we can be reasonably sure about hinges 1, 5, and 6. The weights of the different parts of the structure are known, and it is a matter of drawing alternative thrust lines to see whether one can be found which gives six hinges, located approximately as shown. If such a line can be drawn, the complete structure is on the point of collapse; if a line can be drawn which produces less than six hinges, there could still be a partial collapse; if a line can be found which lies entirely within the masonry, it is certainly stable; while if no line can be drawn which does not pass outside it, the weight of the masonry is beyond its capacity to bear.

It may help to understand the nature of the analytical problem if we think of the corresponding cable structure, which is shown at (c). This is, as it were, a mirror image of the thrust line. It can assume a variety of shapes which depend on the position chosen for the points O and O' in the force diagram, and the point at which a start is made at drawing the cable line at the crown of the nave vault. From then on, the cable shape — or the corresponding thrust line — is built up by the repeated use of the parallelogram of forces, using basically the same procedure as in Fig. 3.9, except that now we do not know the shape of the cable to begin with. The first trial is sure not to fit the boundary conditions, but after a few attempts one begins to see whether the structure is adequate. One realizes, also, how delicately poised are the great Gothic cathedrals, and cannot help marvelling at the intuitive grasp of structural action, and even more at the audacity, of their builders, working as they did in ignorance of the analytical tools we have been describing.

CHAPTER 6

Flow of Stress

THE ELASTIC stresses in a flat plate, or dome, or in any continuous surface or piece of material in a structure, vary or flow from point to point, and we now need to take a closer look at this. The simplest state of stress — uniform uniaxial stress, as it is called — occurs in a thin wire being tested in tension. If we concentrate our attention on a small cubic piece or element of the material with sides cut parallel to the axis of the wire (Fig. 6.1a) the stress on the horizontal faces of the cube is uniform; on the sides there is no stress. The cube elongates in the direction of the stress by an amount e, and it also shrinks laterally by a smaller amount μe, where μ (the Greek letter called mu) is a quantity known as Poisson's ratio in honour of the French mathematician who contributed greatly to the early work in stress analysis. In metals μ is usually about $\frac{1}{3}$; it is less in materials like concrete, but in a material which does not change in

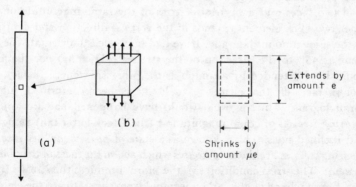

FIG. 6.1. Uniaxial direct stress condition.

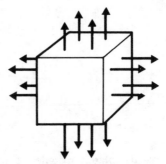

FIG. 6.2. Biaxial direct stress condition.

volume at all under the stress, like clay or rubber which is suddenly loaded, μ is equal to $\frac{1}{2}$.

In the next simplest state of stress, two opposite sides of the cube are also stressed in tension (Fig. 6.2). This is an example of *biaxial stress*. In modern structures, which are commonly made up of thin sections of concrete or metal, the stresses are generally biaxial—or at least it is reasonable to assume that they are—and this simplifies the problem of analysis. But we cannot always make this assumption; inside a thick concrete dam, for example, a small cube of material is obviously stressed on all six sides, and we then have a state of *triaxial stress*.

Figure 6.3a shows a rather special case of biaxial stress—tensile stress σ on two faces and compressive stress of the same magnitude on the other two. The element extends in the vertical direction and contracts by the same amount laterally. If we had happened to orientate the element at 45° to the direction of the stresses (Fig. 6.3c) one diagonal would have extended by as much as the other shortened. In fact, the square face of the element would have been deformed into a parallelogram, which is what would have happened had we applied *shearing stresses* of equal magnitude τ (the Greek letter tau) along the four inclined sides. This is known as a state of *pure shear*, because the shearing stresses are the only stresses which act on the faces of the oblique element. The stress condition (a), therefore, produces the stresses (c) in directions inclined at 45°, and it is found from the statics of the element that the shearing stress τ is equal numerically to σ. Incidentally, since the stresses shown at (a) tend to expand and compress the element

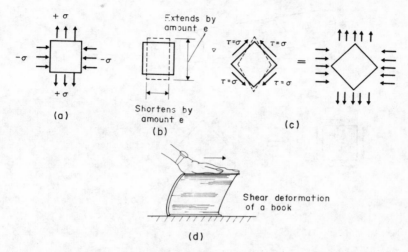

FIG. 6.3. Pure shear stress condition.

equally, it follows that a state of pure shearing stress does not change the volume of the element, whatever the value of μ.

Pure shear is not easy to apply to an object like a book, but we can produce it in a piece of blackboard chalk simply by twisting it. The twisting moment, or torque, which we apply at the ends sets up shearing stresses on the sides of an element with faces parallel to and at right angles to the axis of the stick (Fig. 6.4a). As we have just seen, these are equivalent to direct tensile and compressive stresses, each numerically equal to the shearing stress τ, in directions at 45° to the axis (see Fig. 6.4b). Chalk is a brittle material, and will fracture at a much lower stress than that at which it would yield or flow plastically; so it breaks along a line across which the tensile stress is a maximum, that is, at 45° to the axis of the chalk, giving the familiar helical fracture shown at (c). If we had twisted a cylinder of a ductile material like clay or mild steel, it would have failed by plastic flow along planes on which the *shearing* stress is a maximum, that is, at right angles to the axis, as at (d).

Even under conditions of uniaxial stress like that shown in Fig. 6.1, an element taken at 45° to the direction of stressing does obviously undergo some shear distortion. The stresses on such an element (Fig.

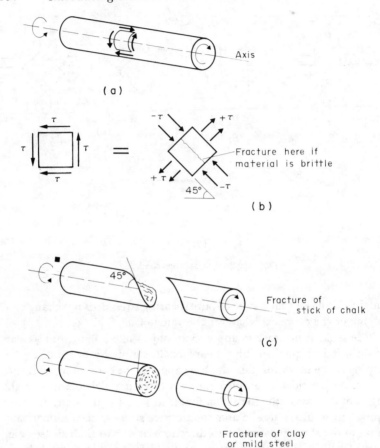

FIG. 6.4. Fracture of brittle and ductile materials under conditions of pure shear stress.

6.5b) comprise shear stresses of magnitude $\sigma/2$ and direct tensile stresses, also of magnitude $\sigma/2$, on all four sides. These are the maximum shear stresses in the material, in fact: if the element were taken at any other angle to the direction of the uniaxial stress the shear stresses would be smaller.

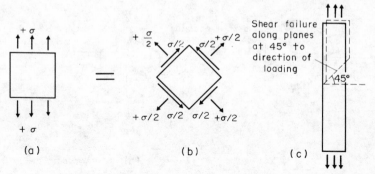

FIG. 6.5. Shear stresses associated with condition of uniaxial direct stress.

Even in direct tension, therefore, it is possible for a test specimen such as a strip of ductile metal to fail by plastic flow, and this will take place at 45° to the axis of loading (Fig. 6.5c). Even if no obvious deformation develops along this inclined direction, the plastic flow can be detected as striations called Lüders' lines or bands if the surface of the specimen is given a high polish.

If the lateral stresses in Fig. 6.3a were tensile instead of compressive, there would clearly be less tendency to shear distortion in the plane of these stresses, and there would be no such tendency at all if the lateral stresses were equal to the longitudinal ones (Fig. 6.6a). Shear flow could, however, still take place along the inclined plane shown in the figure. If in addition there were equal tensile stresses on the two remaining surfaces of the element (Fig. 6.6b) shear distortion on any plane would be impossible, and the element would be simply expanded by the state of uniform triaxial or hydrostatic tension which then existed. Under such stress conditions, which are more common than might be supposed, failure can only be by tensile fracture. As we shall see in a later chapter, this situation can occur in welded steel bridges and buildings, and can cause unexpected failures by brittle fracture. But a smaller stress, either tensile or compressive, on the second and third pairs of faces can also modify the mode of failure appreciably, as we will now see.

The obvious way of finding the compressive strength of brittle materials like concrete and stone — and, until recently, the one almost

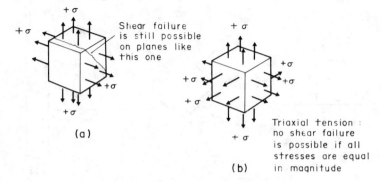

FIG. 6.6. Biaxial and triaxial stress conditions.

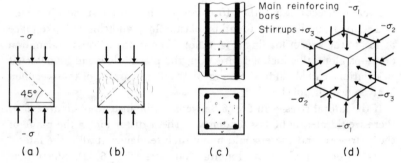

FIG. 6.7. Compressive behaviour of brittle material under uniaxial and triaxial
stress conditions.

invariably followed — is to apply uniaxial compression to a cubical or
cylindrical specimen in a testing machine (Fig. 6.7a). As in uniaxial tension, there is a shearing stress on any plane inclined to the direction of
loading, and this is greatest at an angle of 45° to this axis. The material
usually fails along these planes of maximum shearing stress, either right
across the specimen or — especially in concrete — by the spalling away of
wedge-shaped pieces around the sides, as at (b). But this is not the condition of stress of concrete or stone inside a dam, or in a stratum of rock,
or of the concrete in, for example, a reinforced column, which has closely spaced stirrups around the main steel reinforcing bars (Fig. 6.7c). In
these situations the material cannot expand freely in a lateral direction

as the main compressive stress is increased, and so this stress is accompanied by lateral compressive stresses (Fig. 6.7d), giving the precise opposite of the triaxial tension mentioned a little earlier. If the lateral stresses are equal to the applied compressive stress, no kind of failure is possible, and the material is merely compressed to a smaller volume. But even if they are a good deal less there is a smaller chance of failure similar to that under uniaxial compression.

In recent years a more realistic method of testing rock and concrete has been introduced. A cylindrical specimen is first compressed hydraulically by enclosing it in a jacket and applying hydrostatic pressure by means of water or oil, and then the ends are compressed as well. This makes it possible to control the stress conditions much better, and to simulate the triaxial stress situation which is normally present in structures, except those made up of thin plate-like elements.

We saw in Chapter 2 (Fig. 2.6) that when a specimen of marble is tested in this way the compressive strength of the material is markedly increased and it becomes quite ductile instead of, as it normally is, brittle. And even if the axial stress on the ends of the specimen is tensile, a confining lateral stress has the same general effect on its behaviour. In reinforced concrete columns (Fig. 6.7c), as a result of this phenomenon, it is now usual for the *working* compressive stress in the concrete to be

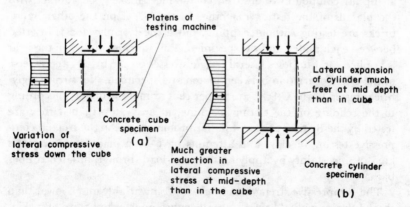

FIG. 6.8. Lateral stresses induced in compression tests on concrete and other materials because of end conditions.

about twice the normal unconfined compressive strength of the material.

Another objection to the traditional uniaxial compression test for brittle materials is that the strengths obtained vary greatly with the method of applying the stress to the ends of the specimen and with its shape. When a specimen is compressed it tends to expand laterally, but is prevented from doing so freely near the platens of the testing machine by friction between the platens and the specimen (Fig. 6.8a). This sets up a lateral confining stress in the material, especially near the ends. In a short, squat specimen like a cube this confining stress persists throughout the depth, but if the specimen is tall compared with its width it is much freer to expand near the middle, and the lateral compressive stress is lower here. Consequently, the ultimate compressive strength is less than that of the cube. In the U.K. the standard concrete specimen is the 6-in or 150-mm cube, whereas elsewhere a cylinder 150 mm in diameter and 300 mm long — twice the diameter — is used. Cubic specimens are on average about 25 per cent stronger than cylinders of this size — enough of a discrepancy to cause trouble in design if the point is overlooked.

Again, in the testing of bricks it is the practice in the U.S.A. to "cap" them on the upper and lower faces with a thin layer of gypsum plaster or a sulphur compound to ensure that the faces make good contact with the platens of the testing machine. In the U.K., on the other hand, bricks are testing without capping, but a sheet of plywood is inserted between each platen and the specimen. This squeezes out when the load is applied, and imposes lateral *tensile* stresses on the brick — the reverse of the effect of friction between platen and specimen. Not surprisingly, bricks tested in the U.S.A. are 30 per cent or more stronger — according to the reading on the testing machine, at any rate — than if they are tested by the British method. Similar problems arise in the triaxial compressive testing of clay, and attempts have been made to reduce this kind of uncertainty by applying the axial load through inflated rubber bags.

The compressive strength of brickwork is invariably much lower than that of the individual bricks — usually only a quarter to a third of it (Fig. 6.9). The main reason for this is that the mortar has a much lower value of E, the modulus of elasticity, than the bricks. Under compression the

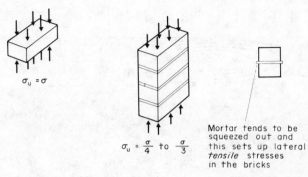

$\sigma_u = \sigma$

$\sigma_u = \dfrac{\sigma}{4}$ to $\dfrac{\sigma}{3}$

Mortar tends to be
squeezed out and
this sets up lateral
tensile stresses
in the bricks

FIG. 6.9. Lateral tensile stresses in compression tests on brickwork.

mortar in the joints tends to get squeezed out sideways, but the friction between the bricks and the mortar prevents this happening, with the result that the bricks are put into lateral tension. This weakens the brickwork in the same way that bricks are weaker when tested between sheets of plywood, but to a much greater degree; and the thicker the joints the weaker the brickwork is. The builders in the ancient world were obviously on the right lines in using extremely thin joints in stone masonry, but, probably because of the irregular shape of bricks in those days, brickwork joints were much thicker than is now considered good practice.

Most stress situations are much more complex than the examples we have been considering so far. In a beam with a rectangular cross-section and carrying a uniformly distributed load, for example, the stresses vary in the way shown in Fig. 6.10; the continuous lines indicate compressive stress and the broken lines tensile stress, and the thickness of the lines is proportional to the magnitude of the stress. (The width b of the beam is assumed to be small in comparison with the depth d, so that the stresses can be taken as biaxial, that is, there are no stresses in a direction perpendicular to the plane of the diagram.) At any point—A, for example—the maximum stress σ_1 in the material is inclined at an angle θ to the longitudinal axis of the beam, and at right angles to this there is a smaller stress σ_2. At the particular point chosen, σ_1 is tensile and σ_2 compressive, but each can be either tensile or compressive. A square element oriented at the angle θ will be subjected only to the direct stresses

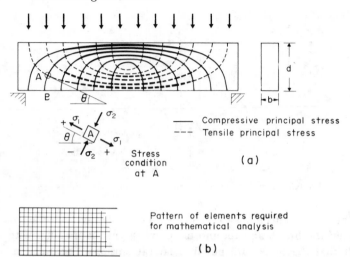

Compressive principal stress
--- Tensile principal stress

Stress condition at A

(a)

Pattern of elements required for mathematical analysis

(b)

FIG. 6.10. Principal stresses in a beam carrying a uniformly distributed load.

σ_1 and σ_2 on its faces, which will be free from shearing stress. If the element were taken in some other direction, the direct stresses on its faces would be intermediate in value between σ_1 and σ_2 and there would also be shearing stresses on the faces.

The stresses σ_1 and σ_2 are known as the major and minor principal stresses at the point A, and the paths which they follow through the beam are called the trajectories of principal stress. From what has just been said, these trajectories intersect everywhere at right angles. Thus the flow of stress is in two directions which vary throughout the beam but which are at right angles to each other at all points. It is unfortunate that (until recently, at least) mathematically it has proved much easier to analyse stresses in a continuous medium by dividing it into a series of square elements than to follow the directions of principal stress in the analysis, because it is the pattern of principal stress which the designer really needs for an understanding of how his structure transmits forces through itself. Some of the finest modern designers (the Spaniard Eduardo Torroja, for example) have advocated the sketching of principal stress trajectories as a preliminary aid in the design of structures with plate- or shell-like parts in which the flow of stress cannot be ascertained by conventional analysis. Of course, one cannot expect to determine in this way the *magnitude* of the stresses at various points, but it is certainly possible to see where stresses are likely to build up dangerously, and in any case the imaginative effort of visualization of stress patterns is always good for the designer.

For example, if a strip of steel is loaded in tension and the stress applied at the ends is uniform, the tensile stress throughout the strip is also uniform and the paths of stress are a set of straight lines (Fig. 6.11a). But if a much wider strip is loaded in the same way (Fig. 6.11b), then the stresses must flow out into the full width of the strip. An important principle due to the French analyst St. Venant tells us that this will be practically completed in a distance from the end about equal to the width of the strip, and this enables us to sketch the stress trajectories with a fair degree of certainty (Fig. 6.11b).

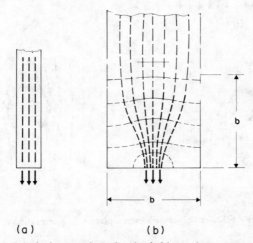

(a)   (b)

FIG. 6.11. Principal stresses in a plate loaded in tension over part of its end.

When the major principal stress is tensile it helps to imagine the stress path as a stretched rubber band. For example, if a wide plate carries a uniform uniaxial tensile stress σ and a small hole is drilled in the middle, the stress paths near the hole are obviously diverted around it and stretched further in the process (Fig. 6.12a). If we consider a small ele-

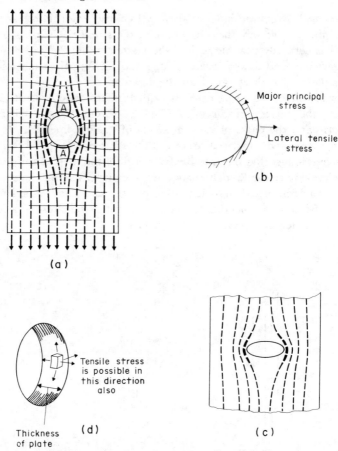

FIG. 6.12. Principal stresses in a plate with a central hole.

ment at the edge of the hole with its sides cut parallel to and at right angles to the path of the principal stress there, it can be seen that, because of the curvature of the element, the major principal stress tends to pull it to the left, into the hole, and that therefore a tensile stress must act on it laterally to keep it in equilibrium (Fig. 6.12b). Also, the major stress paths crowd around the hole and the stress σ is increased in magnitude there. In a very wide plate, in fact, it is known from analyses that the average longitudinal stress is magnified three times at the side of the hole, if it is circular. An elliptical hole oriented as shown at (c) clearly causes the stress paths to be even more sharply diverted, and the stress concentration factor, as it is called, is greater than 3. When it flattens out completely a very flat ellipse finally becomes a crack, and we can see that in a plate in tension a very short crack at right angles to the direction of stress—an inocuous flaw, one might think at first—is a very serious stress raiser which can easily raise the stress some 200 times and bring it up to the theoretical fracture strength of the material. Since, as we have just seen, there is also a lateral tensile stress at the hole, and, furthermore, because of these high local tensile stresses the plate thickness tends to contract near the hole and is prevented from doing so by the material around it, tensile stress is also set up in the third, triaxial direction (as shown at (d)), especially if the plate is thick. We thus can very easily get a state of triaxial tensile stress, in which failure of the material, even if it is ductile under normal stress conditions, is very likely to be by brittle fracture.

Above and below the hole, at points A (Fig. 6.12a) the main stress paths, to use the rubber-band analogy again, tend to compress the material between them laterally, and so at A we have a transverse compressive stress. If the plate were in compression instead of in tension, the transverse stress would be tensile at A. Thus the presence of the holes and cavities, even in material in compression, gives rise to tensile stresses which can increase the likelihood of brittle fracture.

Stress raisers are unavoidable in structures: they occur whenever the stress paths are diverted by a change in shape of the material, by holes and cracks, or by concentrations of loading; and they can cause an immense amount of trouble. The failure of the Comet airliners in the 1950s, and the breaking up of Liberty ships in the Second World War—to mention only two examples—were directly attributable to the effect of stress concentrations arising at small, apparently insignificant details.

Another type of stress concentration is shear lag, which occurs in plate girders with wide, thin flanges especially near the supports (Fig. 6.13). If the flanges and web were not securely connected together, the web would have to support almost the whole of any load itself; the flanges only work because they are joined to the web and are forced to

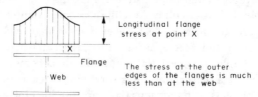

FIG. 6.13. Shear lag near the supports of a girder with wide thin flanges.

act in conjunction with it owing to the shearing force between web and flanges. If the flanges are very wide in comparison with their thickness, the longitudinal stress near the edges may be much less than the stress adjacent to the web, where the shearing force acts, because it never gets a chance to diffuse out to the whole width of the flanges. It is rather like the problem illustrated in Fig. 6.11, except that here the flange stress is being built up from the web continually from the end of the girder inwards to midspan, and the stress at the edges lags behind that at the middle of the flanges all the way—although the lag is worst at and near the ends. In ordinary beam theory we assume that the flange stress is uniform right across it, so that here we have another example of stress concentration, along the junction of web and flanges.

In tension, shear lag can cause yield, fracture, or fatigue failure at unexpectedly low loads, and in compression the danger is that the thin flange plates may buckle prematurely. Box girders, which consist of an assembly of thin flange plates and longitudinal and transverse plates called diaphragms (Fig. 7.13) are particularly prone to shear lag. It is most dangerous wherever the shearing force in the girder is high, especially at the supports and at local points of loading like the cable anchorages in cable-supported box girder bridges (the points 1 to 12 in Fig. 9.31).

In natural structures, one of the most remarkable instances of stress paths occurs in bone structure. In the bones of most mammals, the hollow interior is partly filled with a fine lattice-work of interlaced bone called the cancellous tissue. D'Arcy Thompson relates how in 1866 Professor Culmann of Zurich, to whom are mainly due the graphical methods of analysis of trussed frameworks, was sketching the stress trajectories in a curved crane-head which he was designing. Happening to see an anatomist colleague sectioning a metatarsal bone of the same shape as his crane-head, Culmann saw at once that the arrangement of the cancellous tissue was just like the stress paths he had been sketching. Nature, as Thompson puts it, was "strengthening the bone in precisely the manner and direction in which strength was required". The same phenomenon is found in any other bone which has to carry weight and resist bending. It is particularly clear in the bones of the human foot (Fig. 6.14) which, in conjunction with the muscles of the sole of the foot, act very much like a triangular roof truss of the same shape; but it can be traced in other bones, and in all cases the alignment of the cancellous tissue follows the stress trajectories.

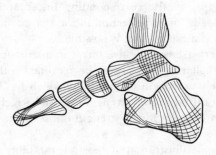

FIG. 6.14. Principal stress trajectories and directions of the cancellous tissue in the bones of the human foot.

The explanation of this remarkable phenomenon lies in the fact that the growth of organic stress-resisting fibre is encouraged by direct stress. This is true of the fibres of an apple stalk no less than of bone fibre—the stalk thickens rapidly as the fruit grows in weight. The trunk and branches of a tree are thick in proportion to the direct and bending stresses they have to carry, and the cell fibres are aligned strictly along the lines of stress, that is, up the trunk and along the branches.

CHAPTER 7

Flexural Instability

IN DISCUSSING cables and their counterparts, arches, we saw that cables, in which the forces are tensile, are inherently stable, whereas arches, where the forces are compressive, are inherently unstable. In a cable or chain, a slight change in the loads merely causes it to settle into a slightly different shape; in the corresponding linear arch, however, any change in the loads, or imperfection in the shape, immediately brings about collapse, if a mechanism is possible.

Wherever there are compressive forces in a structure, the danger of instability and collapse must always be reckoned with. We must now look more closely at a form of instability which has been the leading cause of structural failure in recent times, and which is latent in any structure which depends for its strength on its resistance to flexure or bending.

As a very simple illustration of flexural instability let us consider a straight steel bar of circular cross-section. It is pinned to a foundation at one end A, and pulled at the other end B with an axial force P (Fig. 7.1a). Assuming that the steel is linear-elastic, it will stretch by an amount $\delta = Pl/AE$, and the plot of extension against load will be a straight line (plot 1 in Fig. 7.1d). Now suppose that the bar has short right-angled pieces at its ends, and that the load is applied through the ends of these pieces, instead of through the axis of the bar, as at (b). It now bends the bar as well as stretches it because of the bending moment Pe throughout the length of the bar. This adds to the deflection of B, because the end pieces rotate; the plot of δ against P therefore starts off in a flatter direction than plot 1 (see plot 2 in Fig. 71d). As the bar bends, however, its axis moves in towards the line of the load, especially near the middle, and the eccentricity of loading e gets less. The effect of the bending on the deflection diminishes, the bar's response to the load

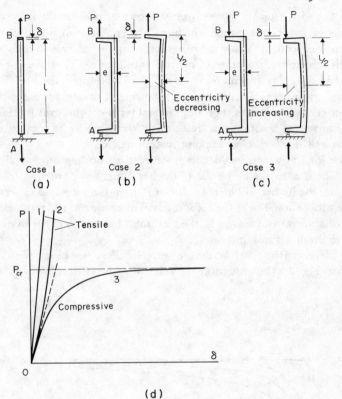

FIG. 7.1. Bar subjected to longitudinal tensile or compressive forces.

stiffens, and the plot of P against δ curves upwards. If the load increases enough, the bar becomes practically straight, as in the first case, and the plot 2 runs practically parallel to plot 1. The bar becomes stiffer as the tensile load increases; we say that the situation is one of increasing flexural stability.

Now let us apply the load P downwards instead of upwards, as at (c). The plot 3 for this case starts off in the same direction as plot 2. But instead of bending inwards towards the line of action of the load, the bar now bends outwards, and e increases instead of diminishing. Thus δ increases at a faster rate as P increases, instead of at a slower rate as in case 2, and the plot 3 curves over as shown at (d). Finally it becomes horizontal, which means that the bar will go on bending and deflecting at constant load. At this stage it has lost its power of resistance to load, and is said to be in a state of neutral equilibrium. The load-carrying capacity does, in fact, increase very slightly as δ increases, but the increase is infinitesimal until the lateral bowing of the strut exceeds about 10 per cent of its length. For all practical purposes the strut has failed, and shortens at constant load just as if it were a stocky bar of mild steel which had reached its yield point in compression.

The load at which this occurs is called the buckling or critical load P_{cr}. The smaller the deflection of the bar under any particular form of loading, the higher will be the value of P_{cr}, and so we would expect P_{cr} to be proportional to I, the second moment of area of the cross-section (see Chapter 4) and also to E, the modulus of elasticity of the material, and to diminish as 1 increases.

If the eccentricity of loading e were smaller, the plot 3 would be steeper (Fig. 7.2) but whatever the value of e, the critical load P_{cr} is the

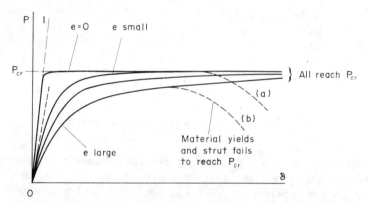

FIG. 7.2. Longitudinal shortening of bar under compressive load for various eccentricities of load.

same. If e is zero the bar is compressed axially, and the graph follows the same line as 1 until P_{cr} is reached, when the bar suddenly becomes unstable and buckles. This is in theory: in practice it is impossible to avoid very slight kinks in the bar or a small eccentricity of loading, and there is always some bending from the start.

The problem of the flexural stability of a straight bar under an axial compressive load was brilliantly solved by the Swiss mathematician Euler in 1744. His formula for the buckling load is

$$P_{cr} = \pi^2 \frac{EI}{l^2}$$

and is fundamental in the theory of flexural stability, so much so that P_{cr} is often called the Euler load. Unfortunately, Euler's work did not come to the notice of practising engineers for another century: in his day engineers did not read the kind of journal in which his paper appeared.

As we have noted, after the Euler load is reached the strut continues to support the same load as the deflection increases. But this is only so if the material of the strut remains linear-elastic. The maximum stress, which will occur at the middle of the strut, may exceed the elastic limit as the strut bows sideways; the flexural stiffness of the bar will then be reduced there, and the load-carrying capacity will *drop*, as indicated by the broken line (a) in Fig. 7.2. If yield occurs *before* P_{cr} is reached, the buckling load is reduced, as shown by the broken line (b). The really serious feature of inelastic buckling, however, is the *loss* of load-carrying capacity once the maximum load is reached. This can result in sudden collapse of the buckled section of a structure and even a catastrophic failure of the whole structure if the force carried by this section cannot find another path.

A tree is a kind of column, and if it grows too tall it will buckle under its own weight. The maximum possible height h of a solid column of uniform diameter d standing under its own weight has been investigated theoretically, and it was found that h is proportional to $d^{2/3}$. Trees have branches and foliage, and their trunks taper upwards. They are therefore not quite like the ideal column of the analysis, but it is a useful approximation to the truth. The theory explains why saplings are much more slender than fully grown tall trees; for, according to it, if, say, a tree of a certain species 9 m high needs to be 54 mm in diameter, a tree 100 m high should be 2000 mm in diameter. That is to say, in growing to eleven times the height of the sapling it needs to be thirty-seven times as thick. The theoretical limit to which a tree may grow is not governed by the compressive strength of the timber—for, as we can see from the specific strength for spruce given in Table 1, this is far beyond the height of any tree—but by instability. Allowing for branches and foliage in an approximate way, estimates have been made of this limit, and it is about 100 m for Columbian pine and somewhat over 60 m for giant bamboo—heights nearly reached by actual trees.

If in our opening discussion on instability we had used a flanged joist instead of a round bar for our column, and arranged it so that it bent as joists are intended to act, with the flanges in tension and compression as shown in Fig. 7.3, we would find that instead of doing what was ex-

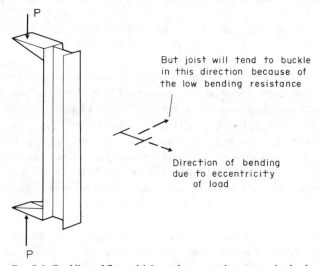

But joist will tend to buckle in this direction because of the low bending resistance

Direction of bending due to eccentricity of load

FIG. 7.3. Buckling of flanged joist under eccentric compressive load.

pected of it it would buckle sideways, and at a much lower load than if it buckled in the strong direction. The reason will be obvious: the *I* value of the cross-section is much less laterally, because the material is not arranged properly to resist bending in this way, and so the critical load for sideways buckling will be lower than that for buckling in the strong direction. This is the situation in a column in a steel-framed building: bending is designed to take place about the strong axis, but it will fail by instability about the weak axis at right angles unless it is restrained from doing so.

Buckling will occur at as low a load as it can, and a section which has much the same value of I in all directions is, therefore, more efficient against buckling than a flanged joist. In steel scaffolding, for example, tubular struts are invariably used, partly for this reason. Efficient strut sections abound in Nature, as we might expect. The quill of a bird's feather, most bones which have to carry heavy compression, and the limbs of crustaceans, are hollow tubes whose bending and buckling strength is very great in relation to their weight. The human thigh bone is thickest in the middle of its length to give as much strength as possible where the bending moment under eccentric compression is greatest. In some tubular plant stalks, as D'Arcy Thompson points out, the arrangement of fibre is so ingenious that the I-value is twenty-five times as great as if the same material had been assembled in a solid core; and he comments on the remarkable resemblance between the 3.7 m diameter tubular members of the Forth railway bridge, with their internal T-shaped stiffeners running longitudinally, and cross diaphragms at intervals, and the tubular structure of such stalks (Fig. 7.4).

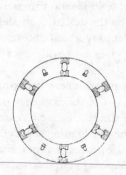 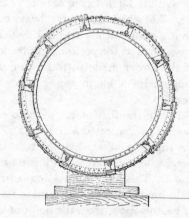

Cross–section of plant stalk
(after D'Arcy Thompson,
On Growth and Form,
Fig 99)

Cross–section of tubular strut of
Forth Railway Bridge
(after W. Westhofen, "The Forth Bridge,"
Engineering, Feb. 28, 1890, Fig 68)

FIG. 7.4. Cross-sections of plant stalk and compression member of Forth Railway Bridge, Scotland.

Flexural instability is a disease of modern structural engineering: it was much less likely in structures before the advent of wrought iron and steel, which were strong and could be produced in thin plate, sheet, and sections. Aluminium alloy compression members are even more prone to buckling because of the low value of E, which is only one-third that of steel; and, as we saw in Chapter 2, there is very little hope that it could be improved by some revolutionary metallurgical process, since it is a basic property of the atomic lattice. Much of the ingenuity that goes into the design of an aluminium-alloy aircraft fuselage is devoted to safeguarding it against buckling in one or other of its many forms. Fortunately, it does not follow that buckling at one point in a structure will necessarily precipitate failure: it has to lead to a mechanism. The crinkling on the surface of an aircraft wing that a passenger first observes with, perhaps, something like alarm is a buckling of the alloy skin, but it is allowed for in the design and is not a cause for concern provided the elastic limit of the material is not exceeded.

Buckling can occur anywhere in a structure where compressive stresses are high. Let us take the example of a welded steel plate girder (Fig. 7.5) which carries two heavy concentrated loads as shown. It is not even a strut, yet it could fail by flexural instability in several different ways. In fact, the possibility of buckling dominates the design. A model of the girder made with drawing-paper and glue, say about 250 mm long, helps a lot in seeing how the different types of buckling can develop.

1.   In the first place, the web can buckle at points where it has to carry a concentrated load (see (a)). The greatest risk of this is at each of the supports, where half the total load on the beam, including its own weight, acts upwards; but it is possible also at the two loading points C and D. This kind of buckling can be prevented by using a very thick web, but this is wasteful in material because, as we saw in our discussion of beam action, from the point of view of bending resistance the web is not at all effective and the material is much better employed in the flanges. The most economical way of preventing buckling of this type is to weld vertical stiffeners to the web; these act as struts in combination with part of the web around them. In the old days of riveting they were of angle section, because this was the only stiff section that could be conveniently fixed to the web by this method; but nowadays they can be flat

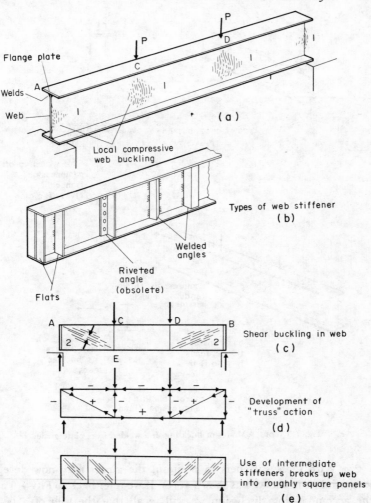

FIG. 7.5. Modes of buckling in a welded steel plate girder.

pieces of plate, or angle or other section attached in various ways, as shown at (b). One can see for oneself how much more effective an angle section is than a flat strip by making struts with paper and loading them by hand.

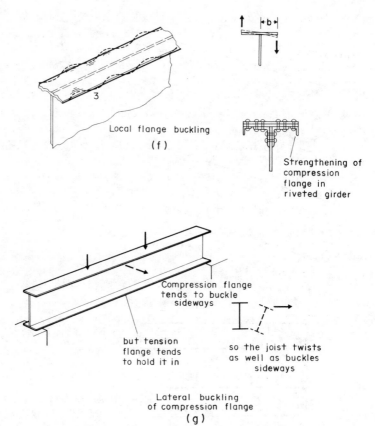

Local flange buckling

(f)

Strengthening of
compression
flange in
riveted girder

Compression flange
tends to buckle
sideways

but tension
flange tends
to hold it in

so the joist twists
as well as buckles
sideways

Lateral buckling
of compression flange

(g)

Fig. 7.5 (cont). Modes of buckling in a welded steel plate girder.

2.   With these stiffeners in position, the girder may now develop long crinkles in the web as shown at (c). If we refer back to Fig. 4.9 and the accompanying discussion we will recall that the web of a beam develops diagonal tensile and compressive stresses to resist the tendency to distort in shear. In a long unstiffened length of web like the panel AC (Fig. 7.5c), tensile stresses run from A to E, and there are compressive stresses at right angles to these which tend to buckle the thin web plate. It used to be assumed in the design of steel plate girders that buckling of this kind was tantamount to failure, and the design was arranged so that

it did not occur; but in the design of such girders in aircraft, where saving in weight is so important, and the aluminium alloy sheet soon buckles because of its low value of E, it was realized that web buckling of this type, though it might look alarming, was not in itself serious. Even if the compressive resistance of the web is entirely lost, the diagonal tension remains, and can be regarded as a kind of rather diffuse diagonal web member, as we saw in Chapter 4. In conjunction with the vertical stiffeners and the flanges, these tension fields form a balanced set of members very much like a triangulated truss, which is perfectly capable of supporting the loads, and quite easy to design.

Such long crinkles are, however, unsightly, and the girder becomes more flexible once they develop. It is better to keep them under control and reduce their length by adding intermediate stiffeners spaced at distances roughly equal to the depth of the web, as at (e). The "truss" system which is then developed has diagonals inclined at approximately 45° to the horizontal, and stiffens and strengthens the girder. There is, incidentally, no tendency to shear distortion in the central part CD of the girder, so no stiffeners are needed here so long as the two loads stay equal. Generally, the shearing force is greatest near the supports, and the stiffeners have to be stronger in this region.

3.   The web having thus been taken care of, we may next find that the top flange, which is in compression, develops buckles along its outer edges, especially in the middle part CD where the compressive stress is greatest (Fig. 7.5f). If the width b of the flange on either side of the web is too great in relation to its thickness, the edge crinkles up and down. In riveted girders this was often prevented by angles attached to the edges, but it is generally controlled by keeping the outstanding distance b within bounds. A free edge of a thin plate in compression is always liable to buckle in this way, and in a major box girder bridge under construction in 1970 it was one of the contributory causes of a disastrous failure.

4.   The top flange of the girder is subjected to a compressive force which is greatest in the central section CD and diminishes to nothing at the ends. It is thus a strut, and like all struts tends to buckle as a whole. If it were free to buckle downwards it would do so because it is weakest in this direction, but it is prevented from doing so by the resistance of the beam. So it takes the only course open to it and tries to buckle

sideways, as shown at (g). But the lower flange, which is in tension, resists this tendency, and so the girder is forced to *twist* as well as bend sideways. The compressive stress in the top flange at which lateral buckling starts therefore depends on both the lateral bending resistance of the beam and its resistance to twisting. In fact, it is found that the buckling stress is proportional to the square root of the product of these two quantities.

The torsional resistance, particularly, is critical in this form of instability. We can get some idea of torsional resistance if we take a thin cardboard roll about 250 mm long such as is used to carry paper towelling, and try to twist it by gripping it at the ends (Fig. 7.6a). It offers a certain resistance to twisting. Now cut it open from end to end, and try twisting it again; the resistance is now much less than before. What has happened is broadly as follows: in the closed tube, diagonal tensile and compressive stresses are set up much as in the stick of chalk in Fig. 6.4, and these run round the tube from end to end in continuous opposition to the twisting torque at the ends. But if the tube is cut these stresses cannot develop, and the resistance to twisting is greatly reduced. For this reason any closed section like a tube or box has high torsional resistance, and any open section—a flat plate, joist, angle, etc.—is weak in torsion. This is one reason why box girders are now so commonly used in steel and concrete bridges: their high torsional strength means that lateral buckling is much less of a problem than in the traditional plate girder. Furthermore, it is possible to use much wider flanges without any danger of edge buckling, so that greater bending resistance can be developed. One must admire Robert Stephenson for his wisdom in choosing a box section for the great girders of his Menai Bridge (Fig. 7.7), or Brunel for the tubular compression members of the Saltash trusses.

A straight strut which is weak torsionally can fail even though it is strong in every other respect. For example, a mast consisting of vertical members connected by light bracing may be perfectly safe against buckling as a complete unit, or against buckling of the individual members as struts on their own, and yet can fail by *twisting* of the central section midway down the mast. This will happen if the bracing is too weak to resist the tendency to twist, or if the connections are weak. The Tay Bridge piers which collapsed in 1879 were of this type (Fig.

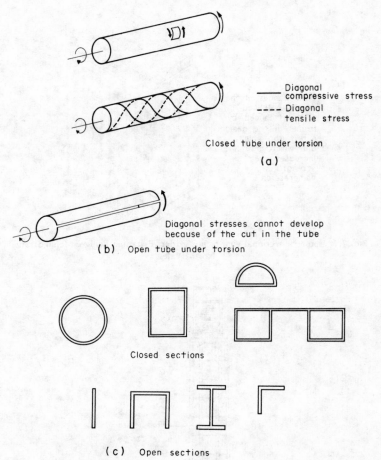

Diagonal compressive stress

Diagonal tensile stress

Closed tube under torsion

(a)

Diagonal stresses cannot develop because of the cut in the tube

(b) Open tube under torsion

Closed sections

(c) Open sections

FIG. 7.6. Torsional stiffness of closed and open tubular sections.

7.8) and there was ample evidence of bad workmanship—slack tie rods, faulty joints, and so on. Torsional instability could have been at least a contributory factor in the disaster.

The design of bracing in built-up struts is, in fact, a matter which does not always get the attention it should, partly, perhaps, because it is rather difficult to work out from first principles how strong the bracing

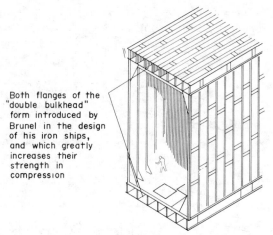

Both flanges of the "double bulkhead" form introduced by Brunel in the design of his iron ships, and which greatly increases their strength in compression

FIG. 7.7. Isometric sectional view of box girder, Britannia Bridge, Menai Straits, North Wales.

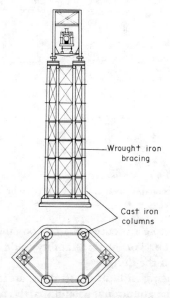

Wrought iron bracing

Cast iron columns

FIG. 7.8. Plan and section of one of the iron piers supporting the high girders of the Tay Railway Bridge, Scotland.

should be. To take an example, Fig. 7.9 shows a built-up strut made from four angle sections joined together by flat lacing bars—a type of compression member which can be seen in many steel trussed bridges.

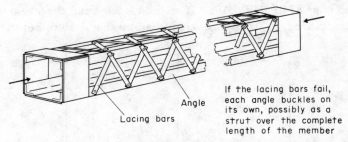

Angle

Lacing bars

If the lacing bars fail, each angle buckles on its own, possibly as a strut over the complete length of the member

FIG. 7.9. Latticed strut.

Apart from the danger of torsional instability, it must be remembered that in design it is assumed that the four angles and the lacing act as a rigidly connected unit. This means that when bending occurs, as it invariably does to some extent in any strut, the complete section is assumed to act as a beam, each flange consisting of two angles, and the lacing acting as the web. If the lacing is not strong enough to perform this function, it could fail, by individual bars buckling (if in compression) or fracturing (if in tension) or by failure of the connections between lacing bars and angles. In this case each angle would buckle on its own between the ends of the strut, at a much lower load than that for which the member was designed. It was essentially failure of inadequately designed lacing bars in a built-up compression member which led to the collapse of the first Quebec Bridge, so that the question is far from being a mere academic speculation. This underlines one of the most important facts about structural design: that the smallest details are every bit as important as the broad over-all calculation of the forces in members, or the variation of bending moment across an entire span. Indeed, most structural failures can be traced to defective design or construction at some detail: very few have been due to errors in the over-all design.

One of the challenging features of flexural instability is that whereas structures in general seem to do their best to delay the onset of other kinds of failure as long as possible—the almost reluctant formation of one hinge after another in plastic collapse illustrates this — the case is different where buckling is involved. The structure will always buckle at the lowest load possible, perhaps in some way quite unsuspected by the designer. The pin-jointed strut studied by Euler has, as we saw, a critical load of $\pi^2 EI/1^2$ (Fig. 7.10a). If one end is fixed and the other end remains pinned, P_{cr} is approximately doubled (Fig. 7.10b). But this only

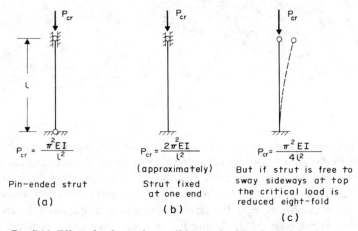

$$P_{cr} = \frac{\pi^2 EI}{l^2}$$

Pin-ended strut

(a)

$$P_{cr} = \frac{2\pi^2 EI}{l^2}$$

(approximately)

Strut fixed
at one end

(b)

$$P_{cr} = \frac{\pi^2 EI}{4l^2}$$

But if strut is free to sway sideways at top the critical load is reduced eight-fold

(c)

FIG. 7.10. Effect of end restraint conditions on buckling load of simple strut.

applies if the pinned end is prevented from moving sideways. If it is free to do so the critical load is only one-eighth of this (Fig. 7.10c); and if it is free to buckle in this way it will certainly do so. For example, let us consider a steel-framed factory building (Fig. 7.11a), in which each frame consists of a joist section. If the gantry crane in the building picked up too great a load, the columns might buckle as shown in Fig. 7.11b. But they offer much less resistance to collapse if they sway sideways, as at (c), and this is how failure will take place unless the frames are braced in some way which prevents this kind of movement. But a column could still buckle in the longitudinal direction of the building, as at (d), if its bending resistance was weak enough and the restraint against this mode of failure was insufficient. These possibilities, and others, have to be watched closely by the designer.

One of the critical aspects of the design of multi-storey framed buildings is their weakness against lateral instability. Although it has

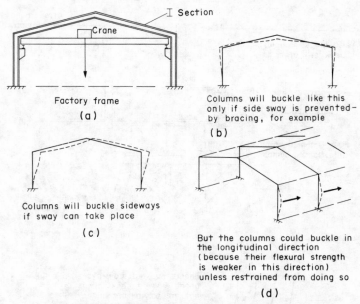

Factory frame
(a)

Columns will buckle like this only if side sway is prevented— by bracing, for example
(b)

Columns will buckle sideways if sway can take place
(c)

But the columns could buckle in the longitudinal direction (because their flexural strength is weaker in this direction) unless restrained from doing so
(d)

FIG. 7.11. Possible modes of buckling in steel factory frame.

long been known that a column is much weaker if allowed to sway sideways than if prevented from swaying, it has only been in the last 20 years or so that designers have actively sought to inhibit sway by solid brick or concrete walls, by strong central cores around lifts and stairs, or by bracing or other means (*v.* Chapter 10). In the 100-storey John Hancock building in Chicago (Fig. 10.12) the structural necessity for some form of bracing was turned into what some people consider an architectural virtue; but usually sway is prevented by less obtrusive means. Quite apart from the greatly improved rigidity and stability which results from the absence of sway, the columns are relieved of the heavy bending moments caused by wind pressure, and can be made substantially lighter in section, especially in the lower storeys.

Any compression member will buckle sideways if it is free to do so. In a bridge under construction in Canada, the work was supported by steel trestles standing on grillages consisting of two layers of short lengths of steel joist above a piled foundation (Fig. 7.12). Packing was supposed to

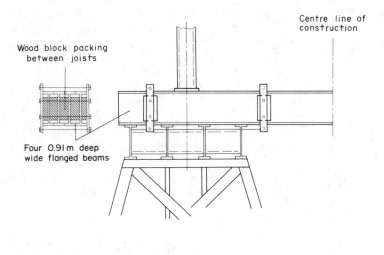

Centre line of
construction

Wood block packing
between joists

Four 0.91 m deep
wide flanged beams

Beams buckled sideways
because wood packing was
not properly fitted under
the flanges and also because
wood is too flexible a material
to support the webs of steel joists

FIG. 7.12. Failure of construction trestle owing to lateral buckling of grillage
joists.

have been inserted between the joists in each layer to keep the webs
upright, but some was not properly fitted. As a result the webs buckled
sideways at a low load and the trestle and the construction above collapsed, with loss of life. Structural failure from instability during construction is too common, and it is usually because the temporary scaffolding and supports are not designed as carefully as they should be.

All forms of flexural instability are potentially dangerous, but those
which occur at unexpectedly low stresses and without warning are particularly menacing. This is likely to be the case in structures made up
from thin plate, because the buckling load is very critically dependent
on whether the plates are perfectly flat, and on very slight eccentricity in
the line of action of the compressive force. We saw in Fig. 7.2 that in a
simple pin-ended strut in which the load is not directed along the axis of
the strut the material may yield before the Euler load is reached; the

buckling load will then be reduced. If the strut consists mainly of steel plate from 8 to 16 mm thick, which is the case in box girder bridges, deviations of a millimetre or two from flatness or in the line of load can double the compressive stress.

Figure 7.13 shows a cross-section of a box girder of the type used in many recent large road bridges. The girder acts as a very large beam

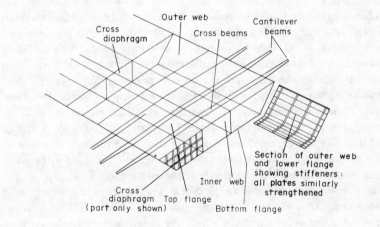

Perspective view of girder

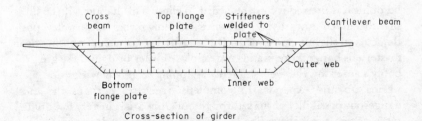

Cross-section of girder

FIG. 7.13. Box girder used in modern road bridges.

spanning between supporting piers. The bending resistance is provided mainly by the deck plate and the bottom plate acting as flanges, and the shearing force is taken by the longitudinal diaphragms and the sloping plates at either side. Cross diaphragms at intervals help to knit the whole assembly into a rigid welded structure, and they also support the deck plate, which has to act as a short beam between successive diaphragms and carry the weight of traffic, which of course bends and deflects it locally. The plates are strengthened with longitudinal stiffeners welded to them.

Box girders are closed sections, and are therefore very strong against lateral instability in bending as a whole. But when such a girder is used as a simple beam the deck plate is in compression. The buckling strength of thin longitudinally stiffened steel plate can be worked out theoretically on the assumption that it is perfectly flat and free from residual stresses. In practice this cannot be assumed. Slight deviations from flatness can markedly increase the bending stresses under compressive forces, and residual stresses (left after rolling and also after welding of the stiffeners) may increase them still further, so much so that the yield point of the steel can easily be reached. Under these circumstances the buckling strength of the plate can be perhaps 30 per cent below the theoretical value. Shear lag, which was referred to in Chapter 6, can make matters worse by causing a concentration of flange stress near the webs, especially where the shearing force in the girder is high. Since several box girder bridges collapsed in the early 1970s strict limits have been placed on the lack of flatness of plates used in such girders.

Another insidious form of instability is snap-through buckling. If the lid of a tin is pressed it may be heard to click. This happens if the lid is slightly curved upwards: the pressure suddenly forces it into a new position curved slightly downwards. On a warm day one can sometimes hear mysterious bangs if one stands near a plate girder bridge; these are probably caused by the web suddenly snapping into a new position as it warms up and expands. In complete structures perhaps the most dangerous possibility of snap-through buckling arises in very flat domed roofs, which can behave like the lid of a tin if badly designed.

CHAPTER 8

Prestressing

WHEN WE plug a wall to take a bracket or heavy picture, or move a row of books by lifting them bodily between the hands, or ride a bicycle, we are making use of one of the many applications of prestressing. In prestressing, we set up an initial, permanent state of stress which makes the structure or other load-bearing object work better than it would without the prestress. In plugging a wall, for example, we make a hole, fill it with a wooden or plastic plug, and screw into it (Fig. 8.1). The screw squeezes the plug against the sides of the hole and sets up a zone of compressive stress in the plug and in the wall around, and this generates frictional resistance to pulling out of the screw.

Although prestressing in structural engineering is a recent development, and has been applied mainly to concrete, it is of much wider and older application than this. The spider spinning its orb web in the

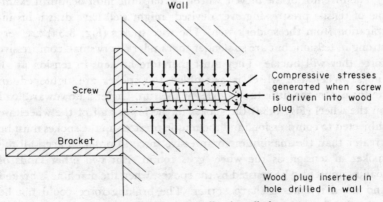

FIG. 8.1. Prestressing effect in wall plug.

135

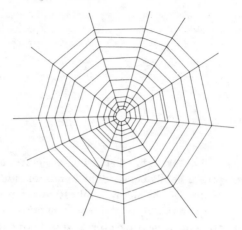

FIG. 8.2. Spider's orb web.

garden (Fig. 8.2) pulls its threads tight to prevent the lower ones going slack when the web is loaded. Unwittingly, the spider applies a *tensile* prestress. The threads are very strong in tension but quite incapable of carrying compressive forces. A load in the centre of the web tends to produce compressive force in the threads below it. Without the tensile prestress these go out of action immediately, and the web is much slacker and more likely to break.

The inventor of the bicycle wheel, perhaps the most beautiful example of tensile prestressing ever devised, might well have drawn his inspiration from the spider's web. The wire spokes (Fig. 8.3a) are very strong in tension, but are so slender that under a very small compressive force they will buckle. They must therefore be kept in tension at all times. When the wheel is assembled the spokes are tightened up uniformly by the little turnbuckles at the rim. Under a downward load on the wheel (Fig. 8.3a) the spokes in the lower half of the wheel are subjected to compression, and the tensile prestress in the spokes must be greater than the maximum compressive force in order to keep all the spokes in tension as the wheel goes round. But two other kinds of loading must also be resisted by the spokes, when the machine is braked and when it takes a sharp corner. The braking force could not be resisted if the spokes radiated directly from the centre of the hub. They are therefore set at an angle to the radii, each pair forming a triangulated system which is able to generate tensile and compressive forces which oppose the braking force (Fig. 8.3b). The prestress ensures that none of the spokes actually goes into compression. Finally, in cornering, a force is imposed on the wheel at right angles to its plane (Fig. 8.3c). This force is resisted by giving the spokes an inclination to the

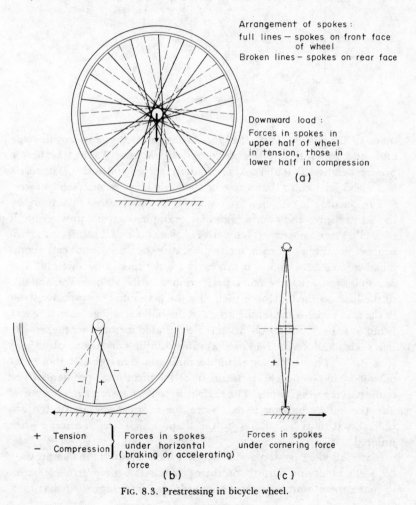

Arrangement of spokes :
full lines — spokes on front face
                     of wheel
Broken lines — spokes on rear face

Downward load :
Forces in spokes in
upper half of wheel
in tension, those in
lower half in compression

(a)

+ Tension   ⎫ Forces in spokes   Forces in spokes
− Compression ⎬ under horizontal   under cornering force
                         ⎭ (braking or accelerating)
                            force
              (b)   (c)

FIG. 8.3. Prestressing in bicycle wheel.

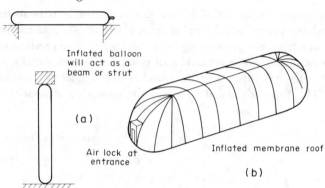

FIG. 8.4. Examples of prestressing by air pressure.

plane of the wheel so that they form triangulated systems in this sense also, and generate tensile and compressive forces. Again, the tensile prestress ensures that all spokes remain in tension and active. The result is a wheel far lighter than those of the early bicycles with solid spokes.

The pneumatic tyre on a cycle wheel is also prestressed in tension, by the air pressure, and another familiar example of tensile prestressing is the child's sausage-shaped balloon (Fig. 8.4a). Until it is inflated it can support nothing as a beam or strut, because the skin cannot carry compressive forces. Blown up, it can carry many times its own weight. The reason is simply that the skin is pretensioned by the air pressure, and until the load on the balloon is such that the maximum compressive stress in the skin exceeds the tensile prestress the balloon will go on acting as a beam or strut. On a much larger scale, inflated membranes shaped like half such a balloon are now used as store buildings and even public halls (Fig. 8.4b). The air pressure inside is maintained marginally above that outside by blowers, to keep the fabric of the membrane permanently in tension in the worst winds. The main difference between such structures and the child's balloon is that since the fabric does not stretch appreciably it must be tailored to the shape which it is to assume when inflated.

Materials like cast iron and concrete which are strong in compression but weak in tension require, on the other hand, a *compressive* prestress to make them more effective. Leonardo da Vinci suggested that cast-iron cannon would burst less frequently when fired if the barrels were tightly wound with iron wire; centuries later the idea was adopted in wire-wound guns. In timber, as the amateur carpenter knows, it is much more difficult to make a tight joint between parts which tend to be pulled apart than between pieces which are pressed together. The problem of making a firm joint between hub, spokes, and rim in wooden cart and chariot wheels was solved at least as early as Roman times by fitting a redhot iron tyre tightly around the wooden rim. It shrank as it cooled and put the spokes and wooden rim permanently into compression, so making a wheel which was far more rigid than could have been achieved by bolting or dowelling the parts together. Thus both the traditional cartwheel and the modern cycle wheel are prestressed, but in opposite senses, because of the nature of the weakness to be overcome in each case: compression in the cycle spokes, and tension in the wooden wheel.

Robert Stephenson's great tubular Britannia Bridge over the Menai Straits (Fig. 8.5a) (completed in 1850) illustrates another aim in

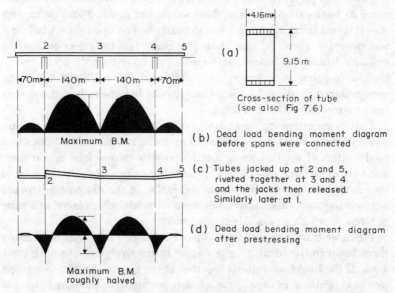

FIG. 8.5. Prestressing of girders of Britannia Bridge, Menai Straits, North Wales.

prestressing. Each railway track was carried inside a continuous wrought-iron box girder of two main spans of 140 m and two side spans of 70 m—very large spans even today in box girder construction, and a brilliant and intrepid piece of engineering for its day. In a bridge of this size most of the stress in the girders is caused by its own weight. The cross-section of the girders was the same from end to end of the bridge. Because of this, it was most important for reasons of economy in material that when the bridge carried only its own weight the maximum bending moments, which occurred at the middle of the spans and over the piers, should be as nearly as possible the same in magnitude, as this would keep the stresses in the girders to a minimum.

The spans were raised into position on the piers separately, and if they had simply been riveted together after erection the bending moments at the piers would have been very small compared with those at the middle of the spans (Fig. 8.5b). Before any connections were made, therefore, girders 2 and 4 were jacked up above their final horizontal level at their far ends, as shown at (c). They were then riveted to girder 3 at piers C and D and the jacks were removed. Girders 2 and 4 acted as huge cantilevers, and their weight put girder 3 and themselves into reversed bending. Span 1 was similarly jacked up at pier A before it was riveted to girder 2. The whole procedure had the effect of creating negative bending moments at piers 2, 3, and 4 roughly equal to the positive (sagging) moments at the middle of the spans (Fig. 8.5d) which were reduced to about half what they would have been had the girders been connected without jacking.

This was prestressing on a truly grand scale, and its aim was to set up a system of internal forces in the structure which would act in opposition to the effect of applied loads, particularly its own weight in this case, and so save material and cost. This objective differs from that in most of the examples of prestressing described earlier in this chapter, where the aim was to protect the material or member from being placed in a state of stress in which it was inherently weak.

When we transfer a set of books from one shelf to another by pressing them between the hands (Fig. 8.6a) we instinctively achieve both these aims. If the books were glued together at the covers and between pages we could lift them at the ends as a beam, without any pressure. But they are not, and therefore there is no tensile strength between successive

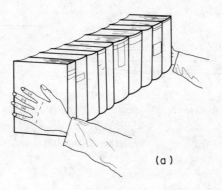

(a)

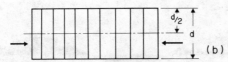

(b)

FIG. 8.6. Prestressing of row of books.

volumes. The pressure which we apply overcomes the tensile stress caused throughout the lower half of the "beam" of books by its own weight, and enables it to act as a unit. It will do so if the pressure is applied halfway down. But in order to lift the books with less pressure we instinctively place our hands somewhat lower (Fig. 8.6b) and in so doing introduce an upward bending moment to counteract the downward bending moment caused by the weight of the books — the same objective as in the Britannia Bridge, but realized by a different method.

Large prestressed concrete beams are often made up of separate blocks strung together by cables or rods of high tensile steel passing through holes left in them, and put into high tension by jacks, screws, or some other means. In principle the action is precisely the same as in the row of books, but a refinement is possible which could not be introduced there. Since the bending moment caused by the weight of the beam and any loading which it is intended to carry is greatest at midspan, the cables are lowest in the beam here; at the ends there is no bending mo-

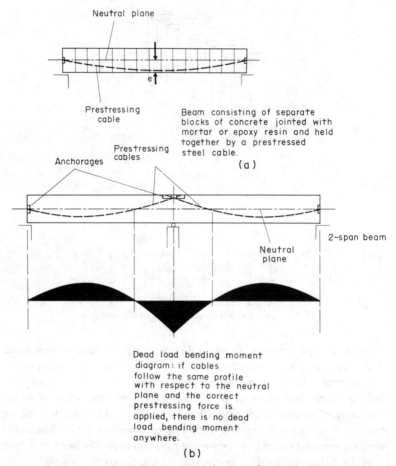

Beam consisting of separate blocks of concrete jointed with mortar or epoxy resin and held together by a prestressed steel cable.

(a)

2-span beam

Dead load bending moment diagram: if cables follow the same profile with respect to the neutral plane and the correct prestressing force is applied, there is no dead load bending moment anywhere.

(b)

FIG. 8.7. Prestressing of concrete beams.

ment to counteract, and the cables rise to about mid-depth there (Fig. 8.7a). Since the bending moment produced by the cables at any point is equal to the tension in them times the distance e of the cables below the neutral axis of the beam, they are usually arranged to take a roughly parabolic shape, because the bending moment due to uniformly distributed loads (the usual form of loading) also varies parabolically from end to end. Even if the concrete is cast in one continuous piece instead of in a series of blocks, the design is similar, for the tensile strength of the concrete is only about one-tenth of its compressive strength and is usually neglected in design.

In a reinforced concrete beam the concrete on the tension side soon cracks when load is applied, and is neglected for design purposes: the beam is assumed to consist of the concrete on the compression side and the steel reinforcement on the tensile side. In a prestressed beam, on the other hand, the concrete is kept entirely in compression by the cables or rods, and so the whole of the concrete, instead of only about half of it, can be taken into account by the designer. This leads to substantial economies in material. The strength and reliability of concrete, too, have greatly improved in the last 40 years, and much higher design stresses can now be used. Furthermore, the position of the prestressing steel in the beam can be varied to counteract, entirely if necessary, the bending moments caused by its own weight. In a simply supported beam, as we saw just now, this is done by giving the steel a parabolic shape. In a two-span continuous beam (Fig. 8.7b) the cables must again follow the shape of the bending moment diagram in reverse. It is then possible to produce a design in which, under its own weight, the concrete in the beam is in a state of uniform compression, and does not go into tension anywhere even under the additional loads for which it is designed.

For these reasons, prestressing reduces the dead weight of concrete construction most dramatically. Large beams in the form of deep joists with webs less than 100 mm thick—just wide enough to accommodate the prestressing steel, in fact—became fairly common after 1945. With lightness and high stresses came flexibility and resilience; concrete could now be used, for example, for springboards in swimming pools, and engineering teachers were able to make wands of prestressed concrete a metre long and 10 mm or so thick which could be waved in front of wondering students like the old-fashioned cane.

If prestressed concrete was such a great advance on reinforced concrete, why was it so long in coming into general use? High-tensile steel, almost invariably used for prestressing cables, was available well before 1945. But it could not be used in reinforced concrete because fine cracks develop wherever the concrete is in tension, and this cracking must be kept within limits to protect the steel from corrosion from the atmosphere. The reinforcement cannot, therefore, be highly stressed, and it is pointless to use anything much stronger than mild steel. In prestressed concrete, on the other hand, high steel stresses are essential. The concrete is permanently compressed by the prestressing steel, so that there are no cracks and therefore no fear of corrosion from the atmosphere. Now the concrete shortens under this compression by the process known as creep (it also shortens because of shrinkage when it is first made, but wherever possible concrete is not prestressed until this is more or less complete). The higher the steel stress the greater its elongation, and the smaller, in consequence, will be the percentage loss of steel stress due to the creep. In mild steel the loss is much too great to be acceptable, but with working stresses five or six times as high, the use of high-tensile steel reduces it to a few per cent and makes the prestressing of concrete feasible.

The concrete also needs to be much stronger than is required for reinforced concrete construction. This is partly because it is permanently under heavy compression, even when the structure is not loaded; another reason is that the stronger the concrete the smaller is the contraction from creep and shrinkage. Commercial production of large quantities of high-strength concrete with reliable properties really dates only from the Second World War, but even then the development of prestressed concrete was delayed for some time owing to uncertainty as to the extent of creep in concrete of various qualities. The practical techniques of applying the prestress — the forces required in large members run into many hundreds of tonnes — also had to be worked out. In the years immediately after 1945 it became almost obligatory for the ambitious young convert to prestressing to make a pilgrimage to Paris and Ghent, where the inventors and patentees of the two rival systems, M. Eugene Freyssinet (to whom much of the early development was due) and Professor Gustave Magnel, held court; but nowadays a great variety of equipment is available for particular requirements.

In the beam shown in Fig. 8.7a the prestressing force was applied *after* the concrete had been cast and had set. This is an example of *post-tensioned* construction. A very important new industry, however, has grown up around the technique known as *pretensioning*, which is particularly convenient for the factory production of large numbers of small- to medium-sized units for floors, lintels, short-span bridges, building frames, fence posts and the like. Prestressing wires are stretched over a long length—several hundred metres, typically—and the concrete is cast around them in steel forms. After a few hours of steam heating it is strong enough for the wires to be released at the ends. The prestress is retained because of the bond between the wires and the concrete, which can be cut into short lengths ready for use.

Beams are only one of the structural types which benefit from prestressing. In a concrete arch the curved axis gradually shortens because of shrinkage and creep under the compressive stress, and this shortening sets up serious bending stresses. These can be virtually eliminated by precompressing the arch by the amount of shortening expected to occur, by means of special flat jacks (invented by Freyssinet) which are inserted in the arch rib at points about a quarter of the span from each abutment. The great arched road bridge at Gladesville in Sydney, Australia (Fig. 3.18), has four ribs side by side, each of which is made up of over 100 hollow concrete blocks. The ribs were erected on falsework and then prestressed by batteries of these flat jacks located a quarter of the span from each abutment. Flat jacks are in effect flat balloons of thin sheet steel. At Gladesville they were inflated by oil under high pressure and the oil was then replaced by cement grout which set and kept the jacks permanently expanded in the arch. As well as relieving the arch of the bending stresses due to shrinkage and creep,

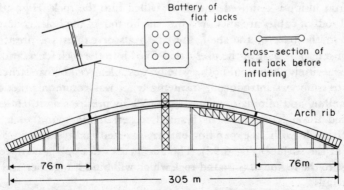

FIG. 8.8. Prestressing of concrete arch (Gladesville Bridge, Sydney, Australia).

the operation also lifted the arch gently and uniformly off its supporting falsework (Fig. 8.8), and so avoided the difficult decentering procedure which in the old days sometimes left stone or brick arches with an unsightly kink or crack at the crown (when for example the falsework was removed under Brunel's railway bridge over the River Thames at Maidenhead, one of the two arches, which at 37 m have the largest and flattest spans ever built in brickwork, sank at the crown, the bottom three brick courses separating by 12 mm.)

Most concrete or masonry dams are of the gravity type. A gravity dam holds back the water behind it by virtue of its dead weight, which must be enough to prevent it being tilted over bodily by the water pressure or cracked on the face exposed to the water. Before the days of prestressing the only way to raise substantially the height of such a dam in order to increase the storage capacity of the reservoir was to add a lot more material to the sides as well as on top: increasing the height by 50 per cent, for example, would mean at least doubling the amount of material of the dam (Fig. 8.9a). Nowadays it can be raised much more economically by adding material on top of the existing profile, perhaps with a slight thickening out below it. The dam is then prestressed by rods or cables which are passed through holes drilled down through the dam and anchored into the rock foundation below (Fig. 8.9b). Large bored piles for bridge foundations are often anchored to the rock beneath by a somewhat similar procedure (Fig. 8.9c). After the steel shell of each pile has been sunk into the rock as far as it will go and the ground inside is removed, a hole is drilled into the rock. High-tensile steel rods or cables are anchored into the bottom of the hole, concrete is cast in the base of the shell, and the rods or cables are prestressed against it. The base of the pile is thus fixed into the rock foundation far more securely than would otherwise be possible. Well before structural prestressing was introduced, incidentally, it was common practice in tunnelling and mining to secure loose rock by prestressing it. Holes are drilled through the loose or fissured material into sound rock, and special bolts with an expanding end are inserted and tightened up by a nut at the surface (Fig. 8.9d). The aim here is to apply a compressive stress to the region of unsound rock which will bind it together and prevent falls.

Prestressing in steel structures is much less common than in concrete

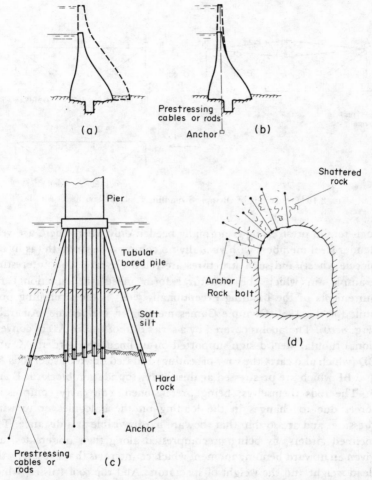

FIG. 8.9. Applications of prestressing in dams, piled foundations and tunnelling.

construction. This is partly because the weakness to be overcome in steel is in compression, not tension, and it is more difficult to apply the required *tensile* prestress than it is to set up compressive prestress, which is easily achieved with high-tensile steel cables. Another reason is that

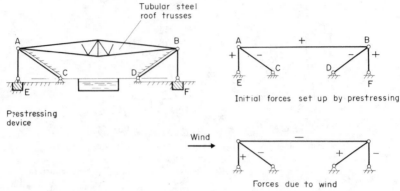

FIG. 8.10. Prestressing of Olympic Swimming Pool, Melbourne, Australia.

such tensile prestressing is normally needed only where there are very slender steel members with virtually no compressive strength (as in the bicycle wheel) and such structures are relatively rare. One interesting example, in which the structural form meets the functional requirements of the building exceptionally well, is the swimming pool built for the 1956 Olympic Games meeting in Melbourne, Australia (Fig. 8.10). The pool is covered by a series of roof trusses AB of conventional tubular steel design supported on inclined steel girders AC and BD (which also carry the rows of seating) and tied down by steel rods AE and BF which are prestressed against heavy foundation blocks at E and F. The rods themselves, being pretensioned, can carry compressive forces due to changes in the loading on the balconies or to wind pressure, and are so thin that they are hardly visible at a distance. The inclined girders, by being precompressed along their undersides, are given an upward bending moment which counteracts that caused by the dead weight and the weight of spectators. And the roof trusses, which are put into pretension horizontally, can be made lighter than usual because, owing to the permanent tension in the main members, tensile rather than compressive stress governs their design. Higher stresses are more permissible in tension than in compression, and so lighter members can be used.

Prestressing has made possible some extraordinary feats of structural histrionics, especially the weird creations which appear for a season at

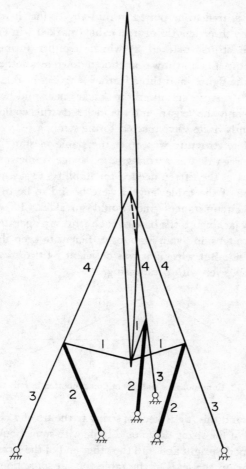

FIG. 8.11. The Skylon, 1951 South Bank Exhibition, London.

great international exhibitions and then vanish. There was the prestressed steel circular roof of the U.S. Pavilion at the 1958 Brussels Exposition, obviously inspired by the bicycle wheel, and the Skylon, the symbol of the 1951 Exhibition in London. The latter was a brilliant demonstration of what can be done with prestressing in three dimensions. This was a cigar-shaped object 76 m high in light steel construction which appeared to be poised in mid-air. In fact it was supported near its base by three lengths of steel cable (marked 1 in Fig. 8.11) and three inclined struts (marked 2) which together formed a sort of triangular cradle. Each strut was anchored down by another steel cable, marked 3 in the figure, and three further lengths of cable (4) attached to the tops of the struts stabilized the "cigar" near mid-height. From a little distance only the "cigar" and the inclined struts could be seen, the latter apparently quite unconnected to the symbol.

The complete structure was quite incapable of standing up on its own: indeed, regarded as a triangulated space framework it was two members short of the fifteen needed for stability, to say nothing of the fact that some of the cable lengths were bound to be in compression under some circumstances and would go slack. It was therefore prestressed by jacking up the base of each strut, an operation which put the cables into tension by an amount sufficient to keep them in action under any wind. But why, if it was deficient by two members, did it stand up at all, even with prestressing?

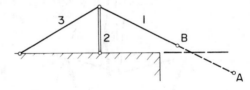

FIG. 8.12. Conditions for stability of post supported by only two stays.

To understand this, tie a piece of string to the tip of a pencil, and anchor one end of the string down on a table with some books (Fig. 8.12). Stand the pencil upright and pull the other end of the string taut. If this end is held *below* the level of the table top, at some point A, and the pencil is tilted sideways slightly with a finger, it collapses. But if it is held *above* the table top, at a point B, it returns to the upright position when the finger is removed, and is therefore stable. Ordinarily the pencil would require another member between its top and the table, not in the same plane as the pencil and the string, to keep it from collapsing: it is the prestress applied by the hand which keeps it upright, and then only if the configuration is right. In the Skylon the cable lengths 1 and 3 correspond to the string, and the inclined strut 2 to the pencil.

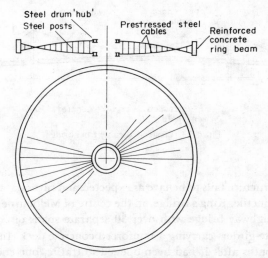

Steel drum 'hub'
Steel posts
Prestressed steel cables
Reinforced concrete ring beam

FIG. 8.13. "Bicycle wheel" roof of Leningrad Sports Palace.

In the last 15 years there has been much development in prestressed steel construction, especially in eastern Europe. "Cycle wheel" roofs on a huge scale have appeared. The roof of the Leningrad Sports Palace, for instance, has a diameter of no less than 186 m, and has 48 radial "spokes" each consisting of two steel cables separated by tubular steel posts (Fig. 8.13). The trusses are attached to a central steel "hub" and to a reinforced concrete ring beam forming the "rim", against which they are pretensioned. The problem of aerodynamic instability of suspension bridges, about which we will have something to say in Chapter 12, seems to have been overcome by prestressing: the first bridge constructed with prestressing appeared in San Salvador in the early 1950s, but many more have now been built, especially in the Soviet Union. Essentially, such a bridge is a pair of pretensioned cable trusses rather than a conventional suspension bridge (Fig. 8.14). The lower chord of each truss is a cable running from end to end of the bridge, and tensioned against the steel or concrete deck. The diagonal cables are tensioned against the lower chord and the suspended upper chord cable, giving a taut cable network which stays in tension in the worst winds.

Very occasionally, as we will see in more detail in Chapter 12, the

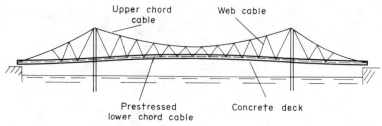

FIG. 8.14. Prestressed cable truss bridge.

steel in a structure fails to behave as expected and turns out to be brittle instead of ductile. King's Bridge, in the centre of Melbourne, Australia, is a long highway bridge with over 30 separate spans of conventional welded plate girders carrying a reinforced concrete deck. In July 1962, only 15 months after it had been opened to traffic, one end span collapsed, and it was found that not only this span but most of the others contained tiny but potentially dangerous cracks. Before the advent of prestressing such a structure would have had to be scrapped. But why not accept the steel as brittle and prestress it like concrete or any other brittle material? Unprecedented though such an approach was at the time, it worked. Concrete blocks were cast at the ends of each span and high tensile steel rods were tensioned between these anchors to give a compressive prestress high enough to ensure that at the critical points of high tensile stress in the girders, where more cracking was likely to develop, no tensile stress would occur even under the worst conditions of loading.

After less than 40 years of development, the techniques of prestressing both in brittle and in ductile structural materials have come brilliantly of age. Structures of a size and form inconceivable a generation ago are being built. The Velodrome at the 1976 Olympic Games in Montreal—by no means the largest of the structures in the complex there—straddles an area 172 m by 130 m with six huge concrete arches (Fig. 8.15) which support the roof through a cellular system of beams. Looking from the air for all the world like some giant fossil insect, the structure is sustained by prestressing on a truly massive scale. The arches were prestressed by a procedure somewhat similar to that adopted

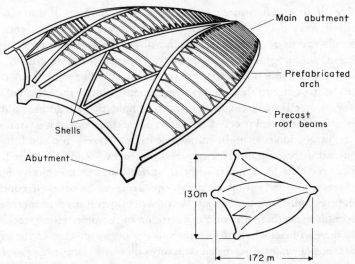

Main abutment

Prefabricated arch

Precast roof beams

Shells

Abutment

130m

172 m

FIG. 8.15. Roof of Velodrome for the 1976 Olympic Games complex, Montreal.

at Gladesville, the prestressing force at the most heavily loaded abutment being no less than 23,000 tonnes.

One question mark hangs over the future of prestressed structures. Early reinforced concrete suffered badly from rusting of the steel reinforcement, partly because the concrete was often poorly consolidated around the bars, but also because, even in good quality work, it cracked under load and some moisture and oxygen from the atmosphere inevitably reached the steel. By the time prestressed concrete was introduced engineers were much more alive to the dangers of corrosion, and in general the steel is very well protected. In post-tensioning, which is used in the great bulk of heavy civil engineering work, the ducts through which the prestressing rods or cables are threaded are filled with cement grout under pressure after the prestressing is completed, and the steel itself may be given a protective coating of some kind. Furthermore, the concrete itself is usually designed to stay in compression except, perhaps, under the greatest anticipated loading, so that cracking occurs only very occasionally and the cracks are closed at other times. But engineers and contractors are only human, and lapses from good practice must occur, if rarely.

Even if air and moisture cannot penetrate to the steel, it is now being realized, very belatedly, that calcium chloride added to the concrete mix in some pretensioned units such as have been used in multi-storey "system" building, in order to make the concrete set more quickly, can also cause corrosion. Prestressed structures are different from other kinds of structure in that they are permanently under the action of very heavy prestressing forces, which literally hold them together. Should corrosion of the steel proceed far enough—and because it is so well protected inspection is virtually impossible in most cases—it could break at the worst affected point, the prestressing forces would be released and the concrete could fly apart without warning and with explosive force. In a recent investigation of many thousands of prestressed concrete structures built since the Second World War, in only an extremely small percentage was there any sign of corrosion of the prestressing steel. But only time will tell whether failures will not occur in some of the many thousands of major prestressed structures now in service throughout the world.

CHAPTER 9

Plates, Shells, and Cable Structures

Plates

The simplest form of plate is a flat slab spanning between two supports (Fig. 9.1). Small reinforced concrete bridges are often of this type. At first sight such a plate appears to be merely a very wide beam, but it is not quite as simple as that. When a narrow beam of rectangular cross-section bends (Fig. 9.2), the material in the lower half of the beam extends longitudinally. In Chapter 6 we noted that when material in the form of a rod is stretched it contracts laterally with a strain equal to μ times the longitudinal strain, where μ, the Poisson's ratio, is about one-third for metals and one-quarter to one-fifth for concrete. Thus the material in the lower half of the beam contracts laterally, and the material in the upper half, which is under longitudinal compression, expands laterally. The result is a reversed or *anticlastic* curvature of the beam in the lateral direction which at any section of the beam is μ times the longitudinal curvature.

If the slab of Fig. 9.1 is uniformly loaded, there is a similar tendency for anticlastic curvature to develop laterally, which would greatly reduce the deflection near the centre of the plate. But in fact this does not occur; except near the free edges the deflected surface is cylindrical, and lateral curvature is completely suppressed. This means that at any point there must be a transverse bending moment per unit length of cross-section which is μ times the spanwise bending moment M per unit length at that point. The suppression of the lateral curvature also induces an additional spanwise curvature in the same sense as the original curvature, with the result that the flexural stiffness of the slab, if it has the same moment of resistance per unit length in all directions, is reduced by a factor $(1 - \mu^2)$. Young engineers designing their first slab concrete bridges have been known to overlook the presence of these

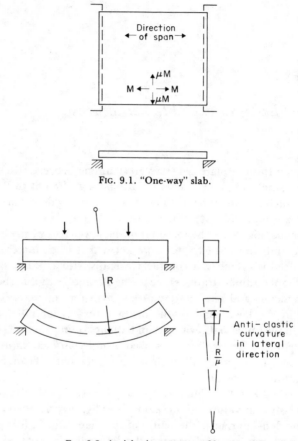

FIG. 9.1. "One-way" slab.

FIG. 9.2. Anticlastic curvature of beam.

transverse bending moments, which can easily cause cracking in a slab not reinforced to take them.

Thus even this simple "one-way" slab has a less straightforward action than one would expect. In a "two-way" slab in which all four sides are supported (Fig. 9.3), and the slab therefore spans in both directions, there is a complicated interaction between the two ways in which it can support a simply supported load on the complete area. If the slab is more than about four times as long as it is wide, the action midway

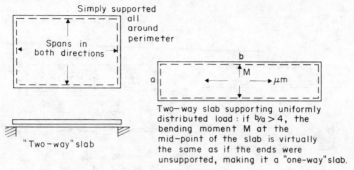

FIG. 9.3. "Two-way" slab.

along is virtually the same (to within a few per cent) as if the ends were free, i.e. as in a one-way slab. In a square plate ($b = a$) the load is supported equally by flexure in the two directions and the maximum bending moment is less than half that in a one-way slab of the same dimensions. The complicated nature of the structural action can be realized from the fact that the corners tend to rise off the supports; to keep the corners of a square plate down requires a concentrated downward reaction at each equal to one-sixteenth of the total load on the plate.

To return to the long simply supported plate shown in Fig. 9.3, if one of the short edges is subjected to a distributed couple M per unit length (Fig. 9.4) its effect dies out rapidly at a distance from the edge greater than a. This is what we would expect from the previous result when the same plate was uniformly loaded: the bending moment at the middle of the long length was virtually the same whether the short ends were free or simply supported. This rapid "damping out" of an edge effect in simply supported plates helps us to understand other plate phenomena: we can conclude from it, for example, that if the short edges of the plate in Fig. 9.4 were clamped or fixed into a wall instead of being simply supported, the maximum bending moment in the slab due to a uniformly distributed load over the whole area would still be virtually the same as in the one-way slab.

Another illustration of the same damping phenomenon occurs if the plate of Fig. 9.3 is compressed longitudinally. Instead of buckling in one half-wave from top to bottom, it buckles in four waves each of length a, as shown in Fig. 9.4. The buckling load under elastic conditions is in-

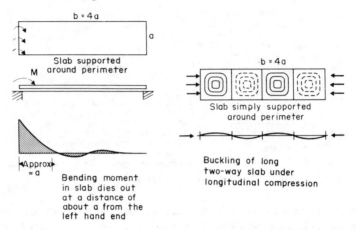

FIG. 9.4. Flexure and buckling of two-way slab.

creased to sixty-four times that when the long sides are free from support or restraint; firstly, reducing the buckling length to one-quarter increases the buckling load $(4)^2$ or sixteen times, since it is inversely proportional to the square of the buckling length; and, secondly, the buckling load of a square panel supported on all four sides is four times as great as if the unloaded sides were free. These facts are important in the design of the webs of plate girders subjected to heavy longitudinal forces, and of load-bearing walls in buildings.

The first correct elastic analysis of a plate problem was made by the French mathematician Lagrange in 1811, when he was examining the submissions of entrants in a mathematical competition set by the French Academy of Science. Some fairly simple problems of rectangular plates were solved by the French engineer Navier a few years later. The analysis of many of the more complicated plate problems which occur in structural engineering, however — including many problems involving plates supported on isolated columns, or carrying concentrated loads, or of irregular shape, or with various kinds of edge condition — only became feasible with the advent of the high-speed digital computer and modern step-by-step (or "iterative") methods of analysis for which the computer is well suited. By comparison, the collapse analysis of flat plates, which we looked at briefly in Chapter 5, is relatively simple.

The elastic analysis of plates which we have been discussing here is based on the assumption that the plate supports the loads entirely by bending action. As soon, however, as the deflection of the plate becomes appreciable in relation to its thickness—say more than one-third to one-half of it—this assumption is no longer valid. Forces develop in the plane of the plate which greatly modify its response to load and increase its stiffness and strength. The effect of this "large-deflection" behaviour is greatest in very thin plates such as are used in box girder bridges, steel ships, and thin reinforced concrete plate and shell structures. Because these in-plane forces are essentially the same as those in an inflated membrane like a toy balloon, they are called membrane forces. Since the membrane is flexible, the membrane stress at any point is uniform throughout its thickness.

A simple illustration of this effect occurs in the aneroid barometer, in which changes in atmospheric pressure are measured by the deflection of the wall of a thin metal box under the pressure (Fig. 9.5). If the wall

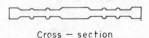

Cross — section

FIG. 9.5. Pressure box of aneroid barometer.

were flat the deflection would not be proportional to the pressure because of the membrane effect, and this would complicate the calibration of the instrument. The wall is therefore corrugated, which is beneficial in two ways. It becomes more flexible, so that the deflection is easier to record; and, since the deflection is now primarily due to bending of the corrugations, it is proportional to change of pressure.

To explain the membrane effect we may first digress a little and state a general principle of structural action, namely, that structures tend to resist loads in as stiff a manner as possible. Figure 9.6a shows two ways in which a straight bar AB of length L and with the cross-section shown can support a load P: as a centrally loaded column or as a cantilever. In the column the stress σ_1 is axial and uniform throughout the bar; in the cantilever the average bending stress in the material is only a quarter of the maximum stress σ_2 at the wall, so that the material is much less effi-

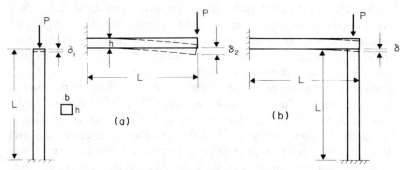

FIG. 9.6. Direct and bending action in a simple structure.

ciently used than in the column. In fact, it can easily be shown that

$$\frac{\sigma_2}{\sigma_1} = 6 \left(\frac{L}{h}\right) .$$

For example, if

$$\frac{L}{h} = 20, \frac{\sigma_2}{\sigma_1} = 120.$$

Furthermore, the column is very much stiffer than the beam; the ratio

$$\frac{\delta_2}{\delta_1} = 4 \left(\frac{L}{h}\right)^2$$

and if

$$\frac{L}{h} = 20, \frac{\delta_2}{\delta_1} = 1600.$$

We can conclude from this that axial action in this simple case is much stiffer than bending action, and also that it results in much smaller stresses.

Now let us use the column and beam in conjunction to support the load P (Fig. 9.6b). Since the two members deflect by the same amount δ at B, and the column is 1600 times as stiff as the beam, it is obvious that it carries practically all the load ($1600P/1601$, in fact), even though the two members have identical dimensions. Thus of the two alternative modes of action open to this simple structure—direct action through the column and bending action through the cantilever—it chooses the direct mode because it is stiffer. Normally the choice in a structure is between bending and direct action, although occasionally another mode, for example torsional action, is an alternative. The stiffest possible mode of action will invariably be chosen.

Some structures can only support loads in bending: the simply supported beam of Fig. 9.7a is an example. Under a uniformly distributed

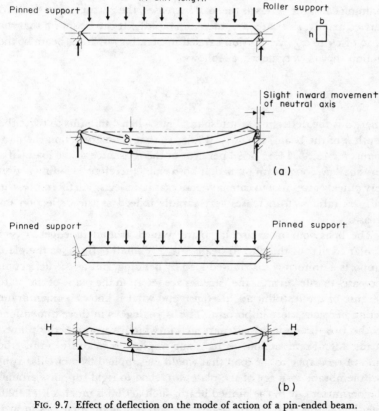

FIG. 9.7. Effect of deflection on the mode of action of a pin-ended beam.

load of intensity w the neutral axis becomes curved, and because the roller support is free to move, there is a slight movement of the end B towards A. Now suppose that this same beam is pinned at both A and B (Fig. 9.7b). When w is small, the load is carried mainly by bending of the beam, but the resulting flexure tends to cause a movement of B towards A, as before. This is now prevented, and as a result a longitudinal tension H develops, and the beam begins to support the load as a slightly curved cable or catenary.

This is a form of axial action, and it is much stiffer than bending. Moreover, in catenary action the stiffness (the ratio load/deflection) increases as the square of the deflection instead of, as in beam action, remaining constant. Thus as the load increases, the portion w_1 of the load carried axially, as a catenary, increases rapidly. It can be shown that the ratio of w_1 to w_2 (the portion carried in bending) is, for a beam of the section shown, very nearly as follows:

$$\frac{w_1}{w_2} = 3.33 \left(\frac{\delta}{h}\right)^2$$

where δ is the deflection at midspan. Thus when δ amounts to twice the depth h of the beam, $w_1/w_2 = 13.33$, so that catenary action then accounts for $13.33/14.33$ or 93 per cent of the resistance to the load. In a very shallow, long beam pinned at both ends, therefore, bending action very quickly gives way to catenary action as it deflects. Furthermore, the stiffness ratio w/δ increases very rapidly indeed as the deflection increases.

The behaviour of a circular plate pinned around its edges is very similar to that of the pinned beam. At very small deflections the plate supports a uniformly distributed load by bending, but as the deflection increases tensile "membrane" stresses are set up in the plane of the plate because of the restraint at the edges, and what is known as membrane action becomes more important. This is analogous in three dimensions to the two dimensional catenary action which we saw in the pinned beam. Membrane action, as its name implies, is in this example the kind of resistance to the load that would be supplied by a circular rubber membrane in place of the plate, attached to rigid supports around the perimeter. As in the pinned beam, such action is much stiffer than bending action, and, furthermore, the stiffness again increases in proportion to the square of the deflection. The ratio of the portion of the load (w_1) taken by axial or membrane action, to that (w_2) supported by the bending resistance of the plate, is found to be approximately

$$\frac{w_1}{w_2} = 2.50 \left(\frac{\delta}{h}\right)^2$$

where h is the thickness of the plate.

When $\delta/h = 2$, for example, $w_1/w_2 = 10$, and membrane action accounts for 91 per cent of the resistance to load.

It should be remarked that the ratio w_1/w_2 depends only on the ratio of central deflection to plate thickness. Thus in very thin plates a central deflection which is very small compared with the diameter or span of the plate suffices to bring about a structural action which is almost entirely membrane in nature.

Next let us consider a plate which *already* supports a uniformly distributed load of intensity w which causes a central deflection of, say, twice the thickness. If we add some more load, this *additional* uniformly distributed load will evidently be supported almost entirely by membrane action, the additional bending stresses being negligible. We can argue further that if the plate were slightly dished when not loaded, with an initial shape similar to the deflected form caused by the load w, *any* uniformly distributed load on the plate would be carried almost entirely by tensile membrane action. If we turn this saucer-shaped plate upside down it forms a very flat dome, and it can be seen that a distributed load on this dome will be supported almost completely by membrane action; in this case the membrane stresses will of course be compressive, not tensile.

Tensile membrane action will develop in a flat plate even if it is not pinned around the perimeter, though a greater deflection is then required for the same effect. What happens is that a zone of the plate near the perimeter acts as a kind of compressive ring reacting against the tensile membrane stresses which are present in the interior (Fig. 9.8a). In reinforced concrete plates, especially thick ones fixed around the perimeter, *compressive* membrane action can develop; because of the cracking of the slab the concrete remaining in compression forms a very flat dome which acts as described above (Fig. 9.8b).

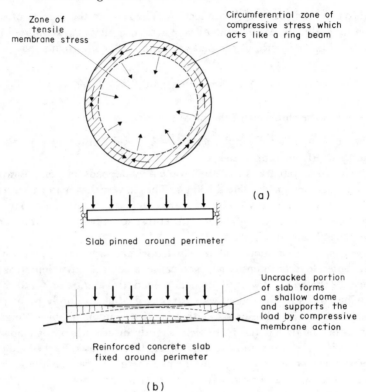

Zone of tensile membrane stress

Circumferential zone of compressive stress which acts like a ring beam

(a)

Slab pinned around perimeter

Uncracked portion of slab forms a shallow dome and supports the load by compressive membrane action

Reinforced concrete slab fixed around perimeter

(b)

FIG. 9.8. Membrane action in a circular plate.

Membrane action in plates, because it results in much more uniform stressing than is the case in bending action, generally means that the strength is appreciably greater than that calculated on the basis of collapse by the formation of a pattern of yield lines. Load tests on reinforced concrete slabs restrained against longitudinal movement, for instance, have revealed strengths from three to seventeen times that predicted by yield line theory. It is, in fact, difficult to confirm the theory experimentally because the membrane action in the test slab obscures the theoretical collapse mechanism. This does mean, however, that the theory can be applied with confidence, because it gives an estimate of strength well on the low (i.e. safe) side.

Shells

The simplest form of shell, the dome, has been used in man-made structures since very early times; but it is only since the First World War, with advances in the techniques of concrete construction and in the understanding of the structural action, that other forms of shell have become common in building. The shell is, nevertheless, a most efficient structural form, and Nature, which always seems to go for economy of material, abounds in examples of shells which act as protective casings for living things. The human skull, for example, is a thin, light, more or less dome-shaped shell; crabs and other crustaceans, and molluscs like oysters, snails, and clams live within very strong shells, mainly of calcium carbonate and of very varied and beautiful shapes and colours; beetles, tortoises, and turtles are encased in shell-like armour; birds' eggs are protected by very thin shells of great strength.

A hen's egg is easily broken against the rim of a cup or by puncturing it with a needle. But to crush it by squeezing it between its ends within the palms of the hands, even when it has been emptied of its contents by blowing them out, is not as easy as one might think. In fact, hen's eggs loaded in this way in a testing machine rarely fail at a load of less than 400 N, and sometimes carry twice as much as this before they fail explosively, after visibly bulging around the middle. Why can such an egg support perhaps 50,000 times its own weight when the load is spread over the surface in this way, yet only a tiny fraction of this if punctured with a needle?

The explanation lies partly in the earlier discussion on large deflections of plates. A dome, even if it is very shallow, will carry a distributed load by direct, i.e. membrane, action, because its shape enables it to act in this way in preference to the alternative and much more flexible mode of action, in bending. Our argument was confined to the case of a dome of the same shape as that of a deflected plate of the same form in plan, and under a distributed load of the same nature as that on the plate. In fact, however, a dome is capable of carrying by membrane action a variety of distributed loads.

We can explain why in the following way. A flexible cable supporting a distributed load takes up a definite shape; if the load varies the shape changes (Fig. 9.9a). If a number of such cables of the same length are hung around a circular perimeter and carry identical loads, they

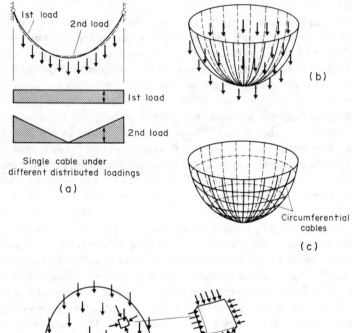

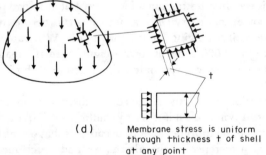

FIG. 9.9. Membrane action in domes.

assume a bowl-like shape (Fig. 9.9b). A change in the load changes the
shape of the "bowl"; for instance, if the intensity of the loading increases
towards the rim, the "bowl" bulges outwards in this region and the bottom rises slightly. Now let us suppose that a series of circumferential
cables is added (Fig. 9.9c) and that these can carry compressive as well
as tensile forces. When the load changes as just described, the circumferential cables prevent the bowl from changing its shape; those

near the rim are put into tension, and those near the bottom go into compression.

If there are so many individual cables, both vertical and horizontal, that the surface is fully occupied, such a system, if inverted, approximates to a thin-shelled dome. By reasoning in this way we can see that such a structure is capable of carrying a variety of distributed loadings by membrane action, that is, by internal forces which lie everywhere in the surface of the thin shell and are uniformly distributed over the thickness of the shell (Fig. 9.9d), just as, in the analogous cable network, each flexible cable is uniformly stressed over its cross-section at any point. The shell has the choice of supporting the loads either in bending, involving variable stress at any section, or by direct action, involving uniform stressing at any section; and since it is capable of direct or membrane action this is how it will act, since this is a stiffer mode of action than bending.

Ideally, for membrane action to take place in a shell under a certain form of loading, it must be thin, and its shape should be similar to that assumed by a flexible membrane under the same loads. This generally requires double curvature, as in a dome, rather than single curvature, as in a circular cylinder; but membrane action is possible in shells which do not conform to these conditions. For example, a closed cylindrical shell supported at the ends will carry a variety of distributed loads by membrane action, as we can see for ourselves by experimenting with an inflated balloon (Fig. 9.10a). Normally a peak (or ridge) in the surface of a shell requires a point (or line) load there: but a conical shell filled with a fluid and freely supported around the rim acts still as a membrane (Fig. 9.10b). The converse of this is never true, however: concen-

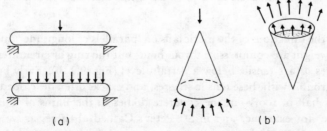

(a)   (b)

FIG. 9.10. Membrane action in cylindrical and conical shells.

trated loads on a shell with a continuously curved surface invariably cause severe bending stresses.

We can now see that if a distributed load is applied to an eggshell with the hands we meet the condition for membrane action that the load must be spread over the surface. The shell will carry the load by developing tensile and compressive stresses uniform throughout the thickness at any point. Thin as it is, it has enough strength to carry a considerable load spread in this way. But if we apply a knitting needle to the surface, the shell must bend near the loaded point because it is not shaped properly there, with a peak in the surface, to carry such a load by direct or membrane stresses. Since the shell is extremely thin, the bending stresses will be very high and the tensile strength of the brittle shell material is soon overcome.

The heaviest loading on most domed roofs is simply their own weight. In a hemispherical dome (Fig. 9.11a) of uniform thickness the stresses

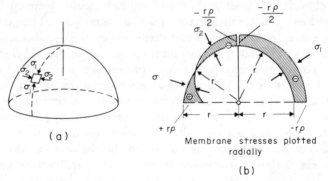

FIG. 9.11. Membrane action in a hemispherical dome under its own weight.

σ_1 in the directions of the meridians or "parallels of longitude" due to its own weight are compressive throughout, but the ring or circumferential stresses σ_2 are tensile below a certain level (Fig. 9.11b). Early builders had trouble with these tensile stresses, and cracks often developed in the lower half of roofs—in the concrete domes in the Baths of Trajan in Rome, for example—and in St. Peter's Cathedral there, as we saw in Chapter 5. But if these tensile stresses can be kept under control by some form of reinforcement, the compressive stresses are much too small to cause crushing of even poor material. The greatest compressive stress in a hemispherical dome is easily worked out. If its radius is r and its thickness t, then its weight is $2\pi r^2 t \rho$, where ρ is the density of the material. This bears down uniformly around the perimeter, whose area is $2\pi rt$, so that the meridional stress σ_1 at the base is $2\pi r^2 t \rho / 2\pi rt = r\rho$.

Thus the maximum stress in the dome is independent of the thickness of the shell, as indeed we should expect, for if we double the thickness and therefore the weight, we are also doubling the area of the rim which has to carry it. And the stress is very small; in a hemispherical dome like that of the Roman Pantheon, of radius 21.5 m and made of concrete, it only amounts to about 0.5 N/mm^2, far less than the concrete can carry in compression (see the Table in Chapter 2). The Romans did not know this, and in the Pantheon first made the dome very thick (more than a metre) and then went to great lengths to lighten the weight by providing recesses in the interior surface, incorporating lighter aggregate in the concrete, and leaving an open lantern at the top. In spite of all these precautions the rim stresses have caused extensive cracking near the base, even though these have roughly the same magnitude as the compressive stresses in such a dome, and might with luck have been resisted safely even with Roman concrete.

The thickness of a modern concrete dome of this span is governed by practical rather than strength considerations—how thin a layer of concrete can be placed which will cover the reinforcement and keep out the weather. It need only be 50 to 75 mm except near the base, where some bending stresses cannot be avoided. Even in much larger domed roofs it is not stress, but the danger of buckling, which is the problem, especially if the shell is very flat. In the largest reinforced concrete shell yet built, the CNIT Exhibition Hall in Paris, which is in plan an equilateral triangle supported at the three corners 206 m apart (Fig. 9.12), a double shell was necessary, the two skins being connected by thin concrete webs and diaphragms. To stiffen the shells still further, they are corrugated, like a scallop shell.

Architecturally, the designer has a good deal of freedom with shells. He can puncture the skin with small windows, or leave a hole at the top, so long as he reinforces the shell at such points to replace the material not there. During air attacks in the Second World War, in fact, some

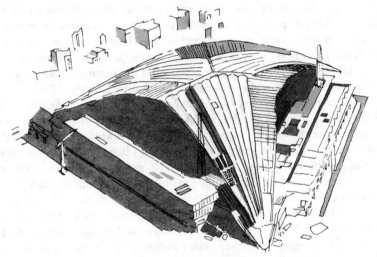

FIG. 9.12. Roof of CNIT exhibition hall, Paris.

large shell roofs on the Continent were pierced by falling bombs without any damage except for the holes. The base may even be arched with great aesthetic effect, as in the dome of the Academy of Sciences building in Canberra, Australia (Fig. 9.13). Thin shells, especially if they are curved in two directions, like a dome, rather than in one direction only, like a barrel vault, have great capacity for carrying different types of distributed loading by membrane action. But, as we noted a little earlier, to carry a concentrated load in this way, the shell surface needs to come to a point at the load. If the concentrated load acts along a line, a ridged shape is needed there. And, in general, if the shell is pointed or ridged, a point or line load is required for the stresses to be purely membrane; without such concentrated loads other loading will set up bending stresses which can be extremely severe. Again, at a free edge the membrane stress at right angles to the edge must be zero; and the shape of this edge may be such that the stress cannot be zero of its own accord there. Severe bending will then take place at the edge, and it will have to be strengthened. In an extreme case the shape may have to be altered, or even the whole structural form scrapped. Shells are a beautiful illustration of the principle referred to earlier in this chapter,

FIG. 9.13. Academy of Science headquarters building, Canberra, Australia.

namely, that every structure supports loads in the way which is most direct and involves least stress and deformation, provided its shape and the nature of the loading enable it to do so.

The Sydney Opera House roofs (Fig. 9.14) provide a spectacular and expensive example of what can happen when this principle is ignored in a large structure. Brilliant in conception and looking on the architect's drawing-board like the billowing spinnakers of the yachts on Sydney Harbour, they were intended to be built as thin concrete shells. But they were sharply ridged at the top, and, like sails, had free edges. On a small scale it would have been possible with some strengthening at the ridge and edges to make such shells stand up under their own weight and the force of the wind. But the great size of the roofs ruled out this solution, and in the end, in order to keep the outer sail-like form, the whole shell concept had to be scrapped and replaced by a series of far heavier precast, prestressed concrete arched ribs supporting a non-stressed skin. The extra weight of the superstructure meant that the foundations had to be strengthened. The end result was years of delay in the construction and a final cost more than ten times the original estimate. Fortunately for the Government of New South Wales, a

FIG. 9.14. Shell roofs of Opera House, Sydney, Australia.

painless and never-ending method of financing the work had been provided: a special weekly State-run lottery.

Even in shells of much more amenable form some bending cannot be avoided at edges and supports. Taking for example a spherical reinforced concrete dome with a half-angle of 60°, for the shell to be free from bending at the rim when the construction supports are removed and it has to carry its own weight, the rim must be supported on smooth bearings which allow it to expand freely under the tensile circumferential stress there (Fig. 9.15a). But this is very rarely done because of the difficulty and expense. Usually the dome is provided with a strong ring beam, as at (b), which restricts the expansion of the shell and sets up bending stresses which have to be resisted by thickening the shell near the rim and putting in extra reinforcement. In the Academy of Sciences building in Canberra (Fig. 9.13) the ring beam takes the form of an inverted U filled with water to provide an attractive circumferential pool into which the arches plunge — a happy instance of a structural necessity being made into an architectural virtue.

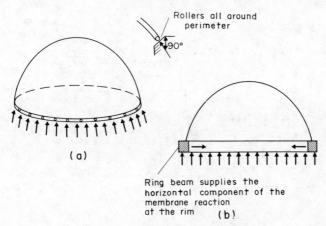

Rollers all around
perimeter

90°

(a)

Ring beam supplies the
horizontal component of the
membrane reaction
at the rim   (b)

FIG. 9.15. Dome with ring beam.

Since the structural behaviour of thin shells became more fully understood after the First World War a great proliferation of shapes has appeared. The spherical dome is still widely used to cover circular spaces. The concrete shell is usually cast on supporting formwork, but house roofs and even quite large domes have been made by inflating a membrane, spraying concrete on to it and deflating and removing the membrane when the concrete has set. But the dome is circular in plan, and quite often, especially in factory construction, square or rectangular areas have to be covered, with support only at the corners. This can be done by taking a portion of a sphere or somewhat similar shape and arching it between the supports, with tie beams to carry the outward thrusts (Fig. 9.16a), but a simpler and more economical solution is the hyperbolic paraboloid. Imagine a square or rectangular piece of trellis lying on the ground and consisting of straight lengths of timber around the perimeter and more straight lengths parallel to these pieces making a rectangular grid. If one corner is lifted and all the lengths of timber remain straight, the flat surface originally traced out by the trellis becomes one known as a hyperbolic paraboloid (Fig. 9.16b). A particular feature of such a shape is that lines drawn on it diagonally are parabolas, humped in the one direction and sagging in the other to form a saddle-shaped surface (Fig. 9.16c). The main load on the roof is

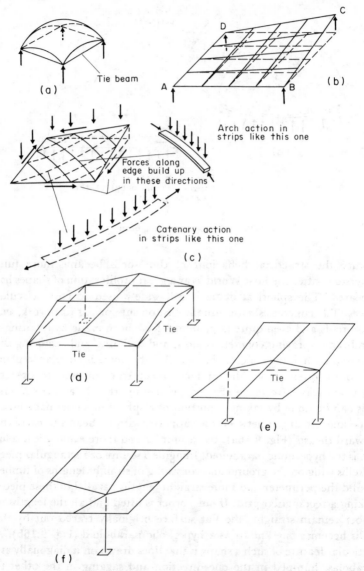

FIG. 9.16. Hyperbolic paraboloidal shell roofs.

its own weight and, in some climates, the weight of snow, and the surface supports such loads in two ways, by acting in tension as a kind of continuous catenary in directions parallel to the diagonal AC, and in compression, as an arch, in the orthogonal direction BD. The pulls and thrusts on the edges from this action resolve themselves into forces along these edges which build up towards the corners; the downward force from the weight is carried equally by the four supports.

In a single shell of this shape the unbalanced horizontal forces from the "arches" and "catenaries" have to be resisted by some means at A and C, or alternatively at D and B. But if four similar shells are combined, as at (d), the thrusts can be made to balance each other out. Ties linking the corners are needed in this design, but in other arrangements only one tie is needed, or even, as at (f), none at all, and only one support.

Constructionally, hyperbolic paraboloids have the great advantage that elaborately shaped formwork is not needed. Fig. 9.16b shows that if straight beams are laid between the sides, and the shuttering boards placed on them, they will automatically generate the curved surface. Structurally, the hyperbolic paraboloidal form is a beautiful example of the fact that, given the opportunity, any structure will support loads by direct tension and compression rather than by bending. A perfectly flat thin plate must carry downwards loads by bending; but if one corner is raised by only one-tenth of the length of a side, membrane action takes over in the diagonal directions, though there is some bending as a secondary effect near the edges.

Cylindrical shells are commonly used to cover rectangular areas. The cylindrical shell (Fig. 9.17a) is a slice taken from a cylinder, usually of circular cross-section, and is supported only at the corners. (It thus differs fundamentally from the barrel vault of Romanesque and Gothic architecture, which is supported continuously along the sides, and acts as an arch transversely.) A complete cylinder carrying a distributed load acts like a beam, longitudinally, as an inflated sausage-shaped balloon does, with stresses which vary in direction throughout the skin but which are entirely membrane except near the concentrated reactions at the supports. Indeed, one way of calculating the stresses in a cylindrical shell is to start on the assumption that it is a complete cylinder, and then to work out the effect of removing the portion below the level ABCD.

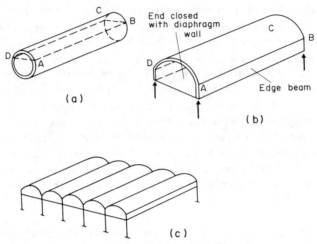

FIG. 9.17. Cylindrical shell roofs.

But this step is a drastic one, because it means that the membrane forces in the complete cylinder at this level must be applied as unbalanced stresses to the free edges. The original membrane stresses are greatly modified, so much so that another method of calculation is to forget about the complete cylinder and start with the actual shell as a beam. Whichever approach is followed, one ends up with heavy longitudinal stresses along the edges AB and CD, which are usually strengthened by reinforcement and, very commonly, by adding edge beams below the original shell (Fig. 9.17b). There is also rather severe transverse bending in the shell, and the ends must be strengthened by diaphragms, usually in the form of thin walls, to enable the end reactions to be distributed into the shell surface without too much bending stress and distortion.

In factory construction cylindrical shells are often built in parallel, as at (c). Each gives support to the others laterally, and this prevents the spread which allows bending to develop. A typical shell roof might have units each 12 m wide and spanning 25 m or more. Except at the edge beams the shells are only about 60 to 70 mm thick, and the edge beams are often prestressed.

Somewhat similar to the cylindrical shell is the folded plate roof (Fig. 9.18). The formwork needed for the construction is cheaper than curv-

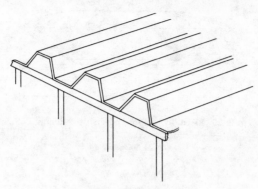

FIG. 9.18. Folded plate roof.

ed forms, but there is no curvature and the kinks between individual plates are serious stress raisers, so that thicker concrete has to be used than in a cylindrical shell of the same span.

In comparison with the shells found in nature, such human efforts as simple domes and cylindrical vaults seem very elementary. Many animal shells are corrugated, like that of the scallop, giving great strength and also great beauty. The coiled shell of the pearly nautilus (Fig. 9.19), with its intricate inner chambers, or even the shell of the garden snail, is

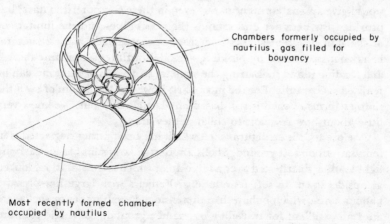

Chambers formerly occupied by nautilus, gas filled for bouyancy

Most recently formed chamber occupied by nautilus

FIG. 9.19. Cross-section through shell of pearly nautilus.

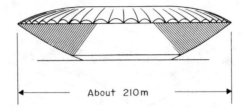

FIG. 9.20. Assembly hall for University of Illinois, U.S.A.

FIG. 9.21. Restaurant shell roof.

perfectly adapted to the life of its occupant. The best structural designers have realized the strength which these forms have, and in structures like the 120 m diameter dome of the Assembly Hall at the University of Illinois, for example, the influence of mollusc shells is clear (Fig. 9.20), as it is in the restaurant roof shown in Fig. 9.21. Such shapes would give an analyst nightmares, even in these computerized days; but provided the designer understands the possibilities and the limitations of shells of different shapes and sizes, and especially if the structural behaviour is checked by building a model in fibreglass or fine mortar and loading it and measuring the stresses, structures of this kind can be realized successfully. For the most part, however, the design of even the simpler forms of shell is still based on elastic behaviour: we know very little about how resistant to collapse they are.

One use for the structural shell which has been rather neglected is in foundations on soft ground. Shells are particularly suitable for carrying light loading distributed over a large area, which is the situation, looked at upside down, in soft foundations. Vehicles with large low-pressure balloon tyres, which behave like pretensioned membranes or shells, are after all excellent for travelling on marshy ground. For single columns inverted hyperbolic paraboloidal or conical shells of reinforced concrete

(Fig. 9.22a) cast directly on the ground, and for lines of columns inverted cylindrical shells, as at (b), have been used in countries like Mexico. Easily the most impressive application so far is in the gravity oil pro-

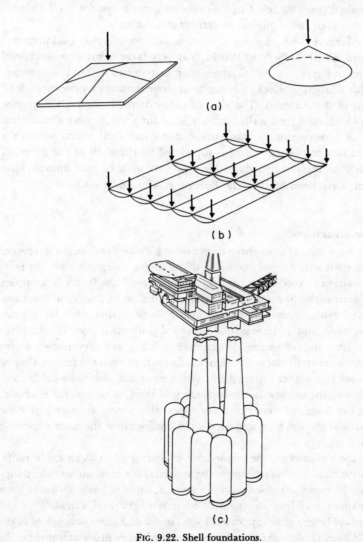

(a)

(b)

(c)

FIG. 9.22. Shell foundations.

duction platforms in the North Sea. The base of the Beryl Condeep platform, for example, consists of a cluster of 19 reinforced concrete cells with dome-shaped undersides each 20 m in diameter which rest on the seabed (Fig. 9.22c). But there seems great scope for shell foundations in much more modest structures than these.

The largest shells in modern construction occur not in buildings but in dams. Until the Second World War very large dams were usually of the gravity type, in which the water is retained behind a massive, roughly triangular block of concrete or stone masonry by the sheer dead weight of the material. The sites of many dams, however, are narrow gorges with solid rock walls, and are ideal for a much more economical form of construction, a thin curved dome-like shell which presents a convex face to the water and is supported by the walls of the gorge. A number of thin-arched dams, one or two with heights approaching 300 m, have been built in the European Alps and elsewhere.

Cable Structures

We have seen that in three dimensions a cable network is the reverse of the shell structure of the same shape. Some designers have, in fact, used cable net models to help them understand the forces in complex shell forms: the Spanish architect Gaudi did so in designing the complicated vaulting system for his Colonia Guell chapel, near Barcelona.

Engineers and architects tend to regard cable structures like the Myer Music Bowl in Melbourne, Australia (Fig. 9.23), as a very modern form: but it is essentially not unlike a nomad's tent, or even the funnel-shaped entrance to a spider's nest. And there were quite ambitious cable roofs in the ancient world — in the top storey of the Colosseum, for example, there are holes for masts to carry ropes which were anchored to stone bollards at ground level and supported awnings over the more expensive seats.

In the circus tent, the immediate precursor of modern cable roofs, the structural and weatherproofing material is a continuous fabric supported by ropes or cables at wide intervals, but this has drawbacks for a permanent building as regards both strength and durability, and nowadays large cable-supported roofs consist of a close network of high-tensile steel cables carrying a non-structural waterproof membrane. As

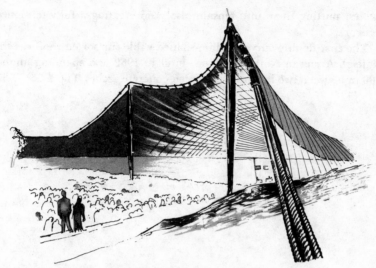

FIG. 9.23. Sidney Myer Music Bowl, Melbourne, Australia.

every camper knows, unless he keeps the guy ropes of his tent taut it will flap in the wind, and he runs the risk of collapse in the middle of the night. Likewise, the cables in a cable-supported roof must all be maintained in tension at all times to avoid destructive oscillations. This can only be done by prestressing. This is easy if the roof is saddle-shaped, like the hyperbolic paraboloid, with curvatures of opposite senses in directions at right angles (Fig. 9.24). Let us suppose that cables are hung between the surround ABCD in the diagonal direction BD, and that a second set of cables is placed over them parallel to the other diagonal AC and put into tension. They press down on the first set of

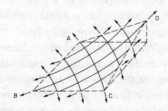

FIG. 9.24. Prestressing of saddle-shaped cable roof.

cables, putting them into tension also, and creating a fully tensioned network.

The first doubly curved saddle-shaped cable-supported roof was the Raleigh Arena in North Carolina, built in 1952 and spanning almost 100 m between two inclined reinforced concrete arches (Fig. 9.25). This

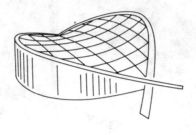

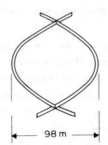

FIG. 9.25. Raleigh Arena, North Carolina, U.S.A.

was followed by the Hockey Rink at Yale University (Fig. 9.26) in which two saddle-shaped roofs hang from a central spine arch, the sagging transverse cables being tensioned by longitudinal cables. More recently, the German architect Frei Otto has used much freer forms supported by posts as well as by surrounding anchorages; examples of his work are the West German Pavilion for the Expo' 67 at Montreal (Fig. 9.27) and the roof for the 1972 Olympic Games at Munich. Interior posts obviously apply very heavy concentrated forces to the cable network. To avoid excessive stress on the few cables which actually intersect at the post, very

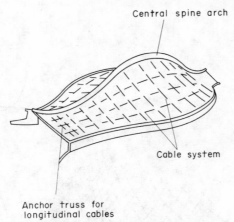

Central spine arch

Cable system

Anchor truss for
longitudinal cables

FIG. 9.26. Hockey rink, Yale University, U.S.A.

strong pear-shaped cables are used which distribute out the reaction from the post into the cable network. Otto uses wire models and soap films stretched over wire frames in designing his roofs, and in the last 10 years or so computer analysis of complicated networks has become possible.

The earliest method of crossing a gap too large to be spanned by a tree trunk was probably by a walkway suspended from hanging cables (Fig. 9.28). Primitive bridges of this kind, made from jungle creepers, can still be seen in tropical African forests and elsewhere. Some of the spans achieved in early suspension bridges were considerable, and fired the imagination; Thornton Wilder, for example, in his novel "The Bridge of San Luis Rey", told the story of five people killed when one collapsed in South America.

Collapse is almost an operative word with suspension bridges: they have been far more prone to failure than any other bridge form. The cause is an inherent lack of stability of this structural form in high winds. Early designers were well aware of the danger and tried to safeguard against it. A bridge which consists simply of catenaries and a light deck suspended from them by hangers (Fig. 9.29a) is very flexible even under a concentrated load moving quietly over it, and stiffening trusses (Fig. 9.29b) which distributed such loads over a greater length of

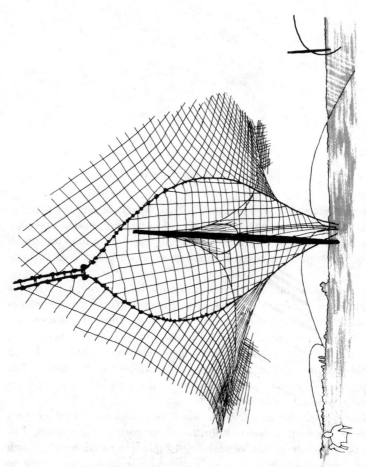

FIG. 9.27. Cable roof under construction for West German Pavilion, Expo' 67, Montreal.

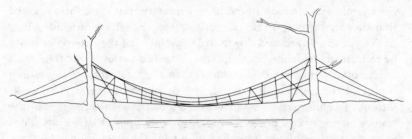

FIG. 9.28. Primitive suspension bridge.

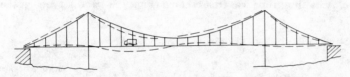

Unstiffened suspension bridge

(a)

Suspension bridge with stiffening truss

(b)

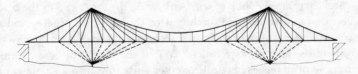

Suspension bridge with
inclined stiffening stays

(c)

FIG. 9.29. Alternative ways of stiffening the deck of a suspension bridge.

the catenaries were soon found to be necessary. But it was also realized that they strengthened the structure against the effects of wind. Alternatively, the upward and downward movement of the catenaries could be restrained by inclined cables, either attached to the tops of the towers or at points below the deck, as at (c). In the most notable suspension bridge of the nineteenth century, the Brooklyn bridge in New York, John A. Roebling and his son Washington, the greatest names in the history of suspension bridges, employed both types of stiffening. They were also responsible for a method of putting the suspension cables into position which was so simple in principle that it has been used ever since. A hauling rope was first erected (Fig. 9.30) and a grooved sheave

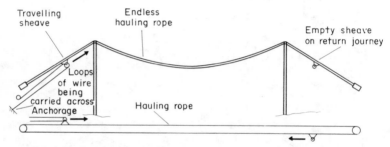

FIG. 9.30. Erection of suspension bridge cable using a "Penelope's Wheel".

known as a "Penelope's Wheel" was hung from it. Wire about 5 mm thick was supplied in reels at one end of the bridge, and the end of the wire was passed over the sheave and anchored back to the abutment. The sheave then travelled across the bridge hanging from the hauling rope and carrying the loop of wire with it. At the other end of the bridge the loop was detached and anchored to the abutment there, and the sheave returned empty to pick up a second loop, and so on, backwards and forwards, as long as required. When the operation was complete the bundle of wires was bound together with wire into a single cable.

Cables made up of many wires had been used before, but the wires had been slung into position individually, and it was estimated that the tensions in the wires in the completed cable might vary by as much as 20 per cent. The Roebling process ensured that they took up a shape very close to the final form of the cable, and were therefore stressed much more uniformly. Hard-drawn wire had the advantage of being five or six times as strong as the wrought-iron links of the early suspension bridges, so that the specific strength, so important a parameter in large spans, was that much greater also.

Not all the later suspension bridge engineers were as conscious of the dangers of oscillation in high winds as were the Roeblings. The disastrous collapse of the Tacoma Narrows bridge in 1940 demonstrated the risk of extrapolating too far into the unknown, and made a profound impression on the engineering profession. Indeed, the more recent developments in suspension bridge design stem from this failure and the investigations which followed it, and we will leave the subject at this stage and return to it when we look at this particular collapse in Chapter 12.

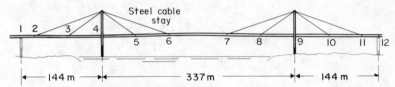

FIG. 9.31. Westgate Bridge, Melbourne, Australia.

Cable-stayed beam bridges are often thought to be a development of the past 30 years, and so they are at least in the great spans which now bestride wide river crossings all over the world (Fig. 9.31). But the basic structural idea behind them — that if the unsupported span of a beam is reduced even by a moderate amount, very considerable economies result — can be seen in, say, the timber viaducts built by Brunel (Fig. 9.32). The raking struts which thrust out from the piers in these fine

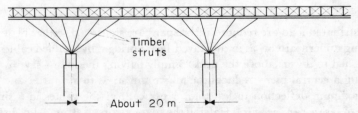

FIG. 9.32. Timber viaduct of type built by I. K. Brunel.

bridges reduced the unsupported spans to perhaps a quarter of the clear distance between the piers. Figure 9.33 shows how dramatically the maximum stress and deflection in a beam carrying a uniformly

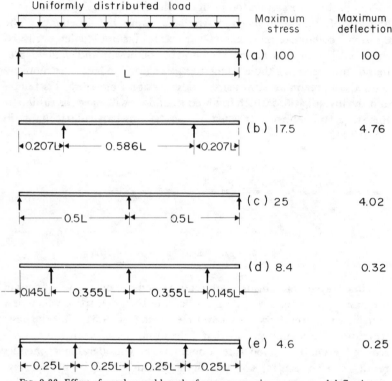

FIG. 9.33. Effect of number and length of spans on maximum stress and deflection in a beam.

distributed load are reduced if the spans are shortened, either by propping underneath or, as in the stayed-beam bridge, by inclined cables attached to towers above the deck. Simply halving the span—say, by adding a central pier—reduces the maximum stress to a quarter and the maximum deflection to less than 5 per cent of the values in a single span, as we can see at (c). Halving the spans again, as Brunel did, brings the stress down to less than 5 per cent, and the deflection almost to vanishing point (Fig. 9.33e). Obviously very much lighter beams can be used, with economies which normally far outweigh the extra cost of the inclined struts or cables and towers. Even without additional supports the maximum stress in a simply supported beam may be reduced to less than 20 per cent merely by moving the supports in a little from the ends, as at (b). This fact is made use of when heavy concrete piles are to be lifted into the vertical position for driving. The stresses due to the weight of the pile in this moving operation may well be greater than any which the pile has subsequently to carry, and they are kept to a minimum by picking up the pile at lifting points located as shown at (b). The same principle has been followed in some motorway overpass bridges (Fig. 9.34) which are carried simply on two inclined supports

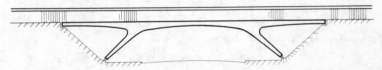

FIG. 9.34. Motorway overpass bridge in which spans are kept to a minimum length.

and overhang them at either end, where they are restrained only against longitudinal movement.

Stayed beam bridges were developed in Sweden and in Germany after the Second World War, particularly for crossings of wide rivers like the Rhine. At Cologne, for example, the street level is not a great deal higher than that of the river, but a certain clearance must be maintained under any bridge for river traffic to pass. The construction depth below the bridge deck must, therefore, be kept to a minimum. At the same time, however, the waterway must be as clear as possible, which means wide uninterrupted spans, which in turn require considerable construction depth. Before 1945 the solution to this problem would probably have been a steel truss bridge (Fig. 9.35a) with the deck supported at the level of the bottom chords, or a suspension bridge. The Severin road bridge over the Rhine at Cologne illustrates the modern approach (Fig. 9.35b). It consists of two steel box girders joined by a steel deck. Over the river there is a clear span of 302 m supported from above at

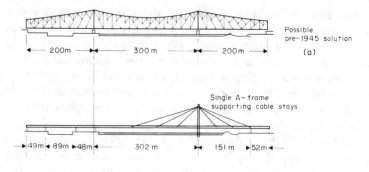

Possible
pre–1945 solution

◄— 200m —►◄— 300 m ——►◄— 200m —►   (a)

Single A–frame
supporting cable stays

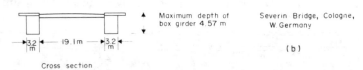

—►49m◄ 89m ►48m◄— 302 m — ►◄ 151 m ►52m◄—

▲
Maximum depth of
box girder 4.57 m
▼

Severin Bridge, Cologne,
W. Germany

(b)

►3.2◄ — 19.1m — ►3.2◄
m   m

Cross section

FIG. 9.35. Two solutions to the problem of spanning a wide river.

three points by steel cables which pass over the top of an A-shaped tower near the east bank. In this way the waterway was kept clear even during construction, and costly underwater foundations were avoided. The cable reactions from the river span are balanced by those from cables supporting a 150-m span at the right bank.

The stayed-beam bridge in steel is now generally regarded as the most economical structural form for spans between 200 and 400 m. For shorter spans staying is less advantageous, while for larger ones the suspension bridge is still preferable. Even in prestressed concrete, in spite of its lower specific strength, spans of over 300 m have been achieved. Before 1945 such clear spans would only have been possible with steel or concrete arches, steel trusses in the cantilever form, like the Forth railway bridge, or of course the suspension bridge. The economic limit of steel plate girders, even with cantilever construction, was less than 100 m. The dramatic advances made since then certainly owe much to the idea of cable-staying, a good deal to the introduction of box girders with thin stiffened plates, and something to the use of stronger steels. But the cable-stayed beam bridge would hardly have emerged, either, before the advent of precise techniques of prestressing, for the tensions in the cables must be exactly those calculated to minimize the stresses in the girders, and they are therefore invariably prestressed. The modern computer is also indispensable for the extremely complex analyses required in the design.

Cable-supported radio and television masts must also be prestressed (Fig. 9.36a). The stiffness of a cable — the ratio of the horizontal pull it

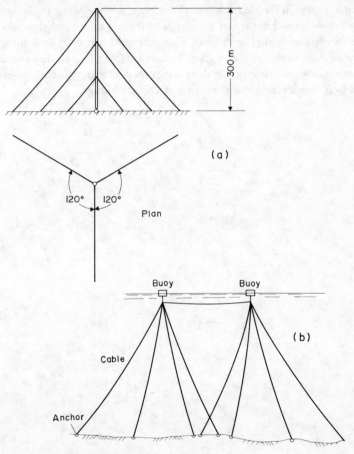

FIG. 9.36. Cable-supported structures.

exerts on the mast to the horizontal displacement of the top of the cable — reduces rapidly as the cable slackens, so that the stays need to be kept reasonably taut to remain effective under a high wind. Too high a tension, however, would impose an unnecessarily heavy compressive force on the mast, as well as requiring a stronger cable. The optimum tensions in the supporting cables, especially in a complex structure like several interconnected masts, can be determined only by computer. Somewhat similar design problems arise in deep-water moorings for ships, in which the floating mooring-points are anchored to the sea bed by cables sometimes many hundreds of metres long, and they too may be interconnected (Fig. 9.36b). Here the problem is to design the anchor cables so that under a given horizontal force from a ship the movement of the mooring-points does not exceed a figure which is determined by the operating requirements of the anchorage.

CHAPTER 10

Multi-Storey Buildings; Foundations; General Remarks on Structural Action

Multi-Storey Buildings

Until the end of the eighteenth century the roofs of most buildings of several storeys in the Western world were supported on continuous walls of brick or stone masonry, and the floors were carried by timber beams resting on these walls, just as they were in the houses still to be seen in the excavated portions of the Roman city of Herculaneum. Cast iron then became available in bulk, and at the same time there was a demand, especially in England, which was in the forefront of the Industrial Revolution, for large factory buildings of several storeys and having larger clear floor areas than were possible with traditional types of building. The solution was found in the use of cast-iron columns in place of bearing walls, and cast-iron beams instead of timber floor joists.

The most remarkable of all cast-iron buildings was the Crystal Palace (Fig. 10.1) built for the Great Exhibition of 1851. Less than a year before the Exhibition was due to open, a designer for the building intended to house it had still to be chosen. Then the head gardener of the Earl of Derby, Joseph Paxton, submitted a proposal based on experience he had gained with cast-iron conservatories. It was accepted, and in 9 days Paxton and his engineering consultants had produced design drawings; after a further 6 weeks construction started; and the huge building was completed in 6 months. It covered an area of 7.7 hectares—four times that of St. Peter's in Rome—and the structure contained 5000 tonnes of cast iron. It consisted entirely of a skeleton framework of cast-iron columns and beams (either castings or of wrought iron) which were prefabricated, interchangeable and demoun-

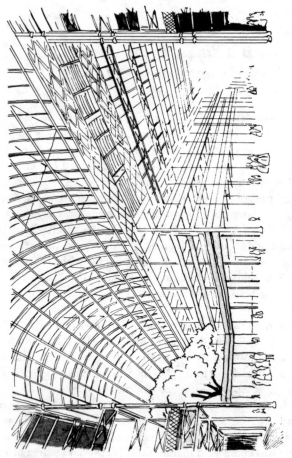

FIG. 10.1. Crystal Palace, London.

table, and was covered with glass sheets. Prefabrication and the repetitive use of a limited number of carefully designed interchangeable parts were not unknown — Leonardo da Vinci's notebooks contain drawings of military bridges designed on this principle — but this was the first important example of what is now known as system building, and it made a profound impression on contemporary engineers and architects. It was also a most impressive illustration of how careful planning could reduce the time required for the design and construction of a major building.

The invention of the elevator in the U.S.A. about 1870 enabled much taller office and apartment buildings to be constructed. At first, in spite of the example of the Crystal Palace, the structure of these consisted of load-bearing walls supporting floors at the various levels. The walls were not designed on scientific principles but by rules of thumb which before long were enshrined in building regulations. These led to absurd thicknesses at ground level: in the 65-m high Monadnock building in Chicago (1891), for example, the walls were nearly 2 m thick at the ground and occupied no less than one-fifth of the width of the building. Such inefficient use of space on very expensive land clearly could not long be tolerated

One of the first designers to use a skeleton frame for tall buildings was the engineer William Jenney. His Home Insurance building (1885), also in Chicago, had cast-iron columns and wrought-iron beams. Steel skeleton frames rapidly became the standard form of construction for the "skyscrapers" of the U.S.A., carrying all the non-structural parts and the loads much as the human skeleton supports the rest of the body and any forces on it (Fig. 10.2).

Methods of calculating the stresses in these highly statically indeterminate structures were available by the turn of the twentieth century, but they were much too complicated for designers to use in their everyday calculations, and reliance was placed on simple approximate methods based on very questionable assumptions. The beams were assumed to be simply supported between columns, although the steel members were usually encased in concrete to protect them against fire, which in fact made the beam-to-column connections virtually rigid. As a result the beams were made too strong and the columns not strong enough, but this fortunately never led to any failures. There were

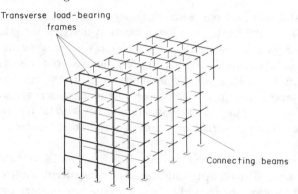

Fig. 10.2. Traditional multi-storey framed construction.

several reasons for this: the concrete protection around the columns strengthened them greatly, the "non-structural" cladding—floors, walls, facade, and partitions—strengthened the whole frame, the loads on the building were almost invariably over-estimated, and the methods of analysis which were used ignored the fact that such a structure is three-dimensional and behaves as one under load (stress measurements on actual multi-storey buildings confirmed the feeling that these structures were usually over-designed). Both the approximate and the more accurate methods of analysis were only developed for plane frames, and it was assumed that each transverse frame supported its share of the vertical and wind loads on the building.

In the 1930s great efforts were made in the U.K. to develop more rational methods of design of steel-framed buildings, but since they were much more complicated and only resulted in small savings in the steelwork (the beams came out lighter but the columns were heavier) they never became popular with designers. The tallest buildings continued to be designed on the same simple approximate lines. Before the Second World War the 102-storey Empire State Building in New York was the highest building in the world, with a height of 381 m. One great advantage of the steel skeleton frame is that it is quickly erected and finishing work can proceed simultaneously on any floor below. The Empire State Building was completed in a phenomenally short time; it was designed *and built* in only 17 months, and the 57,000 tonnes of steelwork were erected between March and September 1930, far more quickly than is usual today. The hidden reserve of strength in such a structure was demonstrated in 1945 when an army bomber weighing perhaps 10 tonnes and flying at 400 km/hr struck the building at the 78th and 79th floors, almost on a column. Although it was certainly not designed for such a force, the frame was unimpaired.

Since 1945 great changes have taken place in the design of tall buildings. One important development up to about 20 storeys is in the use of load-bearing walls without a skeleton frame. In the traditional masonry building the outside (load-bearing) walls support (i) the *vertical* load due to the dead weight of the walls and floors above, and the live load on the floors, and (ii) the *horizontal* forces due to the wind pressure acting laterally on them (Fig. 10.3a and b). To avoid tension in the brickwork the resultant force in the masonry must lie within the

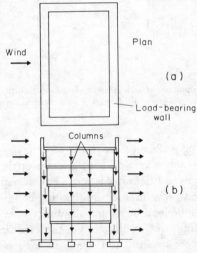

FIG. 10.3. Traditional multi-storey load-bearing wall construction.

middle-third of the thickness of the wall, and this requires very thick walls in the lower storeys. In practice, the empirical rules in building regulations resulted in even more massive construction than necessary.

In modern load-bearing buildings the principle is different (Fig. 10.4). In the very simplest form the horizontal forces from the wind are resisted by walls aligned in the direction of the wind, instead of at right angles to it. Thus in a long building there must be walls running *across* the building to resist the main wind forces. Such walls are far more effective than in a traditional load-bearing building because they have a very much greater moment of resistance, regarded as vertical cantilevers, against the lateral forces caused by the wind.

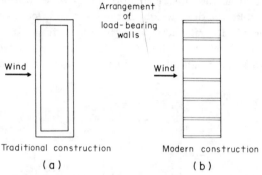

FIG. 10.4. Comparison of arrangement of walls in traditional and modern multi-storey load-bearing wall construction.

The load-bearing walls must be in the same position in plan in each storey, in order to act as vertical cantilevers over the full depth of the building. Unreinforced brickwork is very weak in tension, and the walls must remain in compression under all loading conditions. Wind forces are transmitted to the load-bearing walls directly via the external cladding of the building, and indirectly via the cladding and the floors, which must therefore be stiff, and strong in their own plane. For this reason they are usually of reinforced concrete cast in position to give a monolithic slab extending over the whole plan area of the building at each floor level. The idealized layout of the structural walls shown in Fig. 10.4b cannot be adopted in practice because of the need for doors, corridors, and lift and stair wells. Typical layouts for a long building and a square tower-like building are shown in Fig. 10.6.

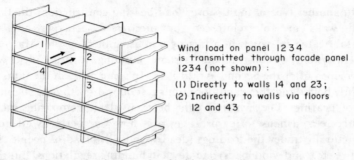

Wind load on panel 1234
is transmitted through facade panel
1234 (not shown) :

(1) Directly to walls 14 and 23;
(2) Indirectly to walls via floors
    12 and 43

FIG. 10.5. Structural action in modern load-bearing wall construction under wind loads.

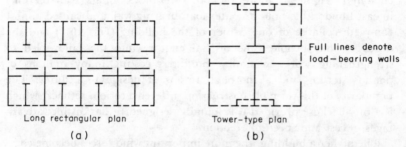

Full lines denote
load — bearing walls

Long rectangular plan

(a)

Tower-type plan

(b)

FIG. 10.6. Types of wall plan in modern load-bearing wall construction.

The strength of modern bricks is such that the thickness of load-bearing walls in well-designed residential and office buildings up to 15 storeys or so need only be about 230 mm even at ground level. Up to about 6 storeys, a thickness of 115 mm may be structurally adequate, though thicker walls are necessary between different occupancies for reasons of sound insulation and fire protection. The need to maintain the same plan form for the load-bearing walls in each storey severely limits the freedom of the architect to plan each floor differently, but in flats and office buildings with repetitive floor plans this difficulty does not arise. There seems to be no doubt that multi-storey load-bearing buildings in brickwork are very competitive in cost with any other form of construction. In some European countries (in Switzerland, for example) hollow units much larger than the standard 70-mm deep brick have been developed, and these further reduce labour costs.

In another type of multi-storey load-bearing construction, the floors and walls are of reinforced or prestressed concrete and are prefabricated in panels in a factory and assembled on site. Many different systems of construction ("system" building, as it is called) were developed after the Second World War. In some of them the units are lightly bolted together, and floor units rest on walls with only 50 mm or so of bearing. The layman might be excused for comparing such a structure to a house of cards. They are, however, perfectly adequate structurally under the loadings (dead weight, live load of people, furniture etc., and wind loads) laid down in building regulations. But their lack of over-all continuity and rigidity makes them extremely vulnerable to loading of an unexpected kind. In 1968 an explosion of gas in a kitchen in the eighteenth storey of a tall tower block of flats (Ronan Point) in east London blew out an outer load-bearing wall and caused almost complete collapse of one corner of the building (Fig. 10.7) and the death of four people. The official enquiry into the failure led to strengthening work on similar buildings costing many millions of pounds sterling and a thorough review of design procedures. The popularity of this form of construction suffered a serious setback, which is a pity because provided it is soundly designed, it has distinct advantages in cost and speed of erection.

The higher a building, the more important wind forces become compared with other loads. At a given value of wind pressure, the bending stresses at the base of the structure, regarded as a vertical cantilever beam, increase as the square of its height. But wind pressures increase with height above ground. In a city area wind speeds may be twice as great at a height of 500 m as at ground level, and since wind pressure is proportional to the square of the wind speed, this means that wind pressures can be four times as great as near the ground. Thus the bending stresses in a 500 m high building might be eighty times as great as in a similar one 100 m in height. Wind forces, in fact, are the paramount consideration in the structural design of very tall buildings.

After the Second World War, the demand for taller and taller city buildings led to a searching re-examination of how such structures could be designed to resist wind forces more economically. The traditional beam-column frame is not an efficient structural system for heavy lateral forces, since the action derives mainly from the bending

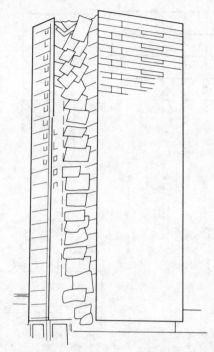

FIG. 10.7. Partial collapse of Ronan Point apartment block, London.

resistance of the beam and columns (Fig. 10.8a). If we consider a much simpler structure, the portal frame shown at (b), it also resists a lateral load by virtue of the flexural strength of the members. The action is one of bending, just as it was in the cantilever beam shown in Fig. 9.6. The material is not efficiently used, and stresses and deflections are high. If, however, we insert a diagonal tie in the frame, as at (c), the effect of this is similar to the propping of the cantilever beam of Fig. 9.6 by the column. The structure is now able to resist the load by direct forces in the members of the triangulated system, and since this is a stiffer mode of action, this is how it will act. The stresses are much smaller than in the unbraced frame (b) and lateral sway is greatly reduced.

In the same way, a multi-storey steel-framed building may be braced against lateral loads as shown in Fig. 10.8d. Not every lateral frame

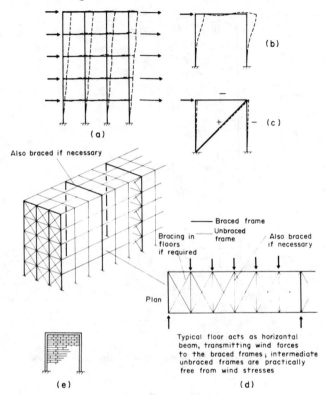

FIG. 10.8. Shear wall construction.

needs to be braced: if the floors are stiff and strong in their own plane (cast-*in situ* reinforced concrete floors, for example, meet this condition) they will act as deep beams in the horizontal plane, spanning between the braced frames and preventing the unbraced frames from swaying. In any case, bracing of intermediate frames obstructs the use of the space in the building and must be kept to a minimum.

Another way of preventing sway in the portal frame of Fig. 10.8b is by building a brick wall to fit inside it, as at (e). The ends of multi-storey framed buildings are commonly protected against the weather by brick or other masonry panelled infilling, and design methods have been developed to take advantage of the ability of such "shear walls" to carry the horizontal shearing forces from the wind. Alternatively, concrete shear walls can be used, with or without a steel or, more usually, a reinforced concrete frame (Fig. 10.9).

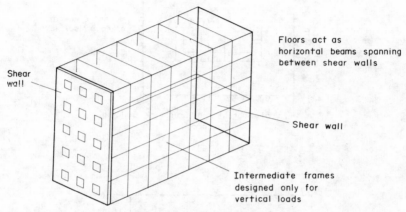

FIG. 10.9. Reinforced concrete shear walls.

For heights of over 30 storeys even these improvements failed to give economically attractive structures. In a modern multi-storey building the lifts and stairs and the plumbing, air-conditioning, and other services take up much space, and have to be enclosed in fire-proof walls, usually of reinforced concrete. In the 38-storey reinforced concrete Brunswick building in Chicago (1962) this central core was designed as a strong tubular vertical cantilever, and the external walls consisted of a series of columns spaced about 3 m apart all around the building, forming in effect an outer tube (Fig. 10.10a). Rigid spandrel or edge beams at each storey level tied the columns together, and the whole vertical structure acted as a single double-tubular cantilever, with the outer perimeter of columns ideally placed to contribute to the maximum extent to the resistance to bending due to wind forces.

The higher the building, the more it becomes necessary to concentrate the structural members around the perimeter, and for heights of more than 40 storeys the framed tube system has been used in a number of recent reinforced concrete buildings in the U.S.A. and elsewhere. In essence this consists of exterior columns usually about 1.5 to 2 m apart

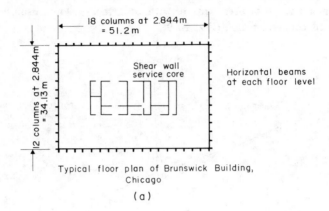

Typical floor plan of Brunswick Building,
Chicago

(a)

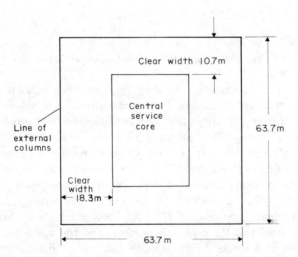

Typical floor plan of World Trade Center
New York City

(b)

FIG. 10.10. "Core-in-tube" construction for multi-storey buildings.

tied together at each floor with deep spandrel beams, giving in effect a hollow concrete tube with perforated openings for the windows, and incidentally rendering unnecessary the traditional curtain wall with its metal mullions (Fig. 10.11a). Such a tube behaves in bending like a thin-walled box beam, and the maximum stresses are magnified by the effects of shear lag, for the same basic reasons as in an I-beam with wide thin flanges (Fig. 6.13). Framed concrete tube systems have been used in combination with shear walls, and in several very tall U.S. buildings the interior is supported by a traditional steel frame. Yet another approach to the problem of design for wind loads was adopted in the John Hancock building in Chicago (Fig. 10.12) in which giant diagonal bracing members straddling each face combined with columns and horizontal spandrel beams to form a huge triangulated framework. But whether such violently obtrusive structural honesty has architectural as well as engineering merit is a matter of opinion.

Such radical re-thinking, in which almost the whole building is mobilized for structural action, can save as much as 50 per cent in the cost of the structural system per unit of rentable floor area, compared with that of a building with a conventional frame. Furthermore, it becomes possible to meet the modern architectural requirement for much wider column-free floor space than hitherto — 15 m or more compared with the economic maximum of perhaps 7 to 8 m with conventional framing. The floor plan of the World Trade Center, New York (Fig. 10.10b) shows what can be achieved nowadays. Halving the weight of steel per unit area and at the same time doubling the clear span is a remarkable structural achievement.

Foundations

Structures of the kinds discussed in this book almost invariably rest on the ground, either directly on rock at or near the surface or on soil lying over rock at some depth. Wise men in Biblical times, according to the parable in the New Testament, built their houses on the rock. Sound rock, indeed, rarely gives the designer any trouble, but foundations on soil usually settle to some extent, and the aim is to ensure that this settlement is uniform and small in extent. Complete failure of structural foundations is rare, though it can happen (Fig. 10.13), but settlement,

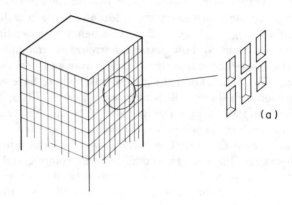

(a)

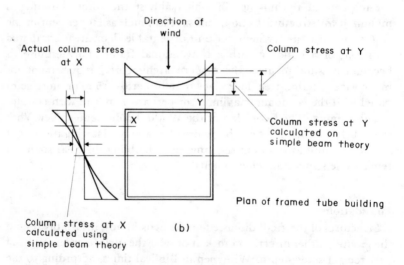

Direction of
wind

Actual column stress
at X

Column stress at Y

Y

Column stress at Y
calculated on
simple beam theory

X

Plan of framed tube building

Column stress at X
calculated using
simple beam theory

(b)

FIG. 10.11 "Framed-tube" construction for multi-storey buildings.

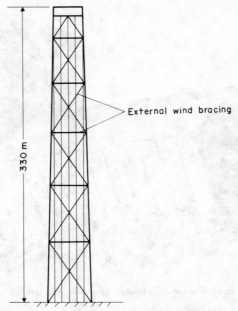

330 m

> External wind bracing

FIG. 10.12. External diagonal wind bracing (John Hancock building, Chicago).

especially differential settling of the various parts of the structure and, in consequence, cracking and distortion of the fabric, has been the bugbear of builders throughout history.

Soil can vary greatly in composition from point to point, even under a single structure. Furthermore, its mechanical properties are profoundly altered by the presence of ground water. Because of this, the scientific study of soils in engineering construction is difficult, and except for a little work by Coulomb and one or two nineteenth-century engineers dates only from the First World War, when the Austrian engineer Karl Terzaghi carried out his first experiments on the strength and compressibility of soils and founded, virtually single-handed, the science of soil mechanics. Indeed, it was not until after the Second World War that engineers generally became familiar with the new techniques, and they were included in the curricula of engineering courses.

Until very recently, therefore, designers predicted settlement by drawing on the accumulated experience of the past distilled into rules of

FIG. 10.13. Failure of Transcona grain silo, Winnipeg, Canada.

thumb based on rather vague descriptions of different types of soil and what stresses they might reasonably be expected to bear. Liberal exercise of the elusive quality of engineering judgement and intuition, accompanied perhaps by prodding the ground with a walking-stick, brought the process of foundation design by less gifted engineers suspiciously close to plain guesswork. Not surprisingly, the mediaeval cathedral builders had endless trouble with differential settlement. What is surprising is that so many major buildings of the past on poor ground are still standing and usable.

In the simplest type of foundation on soil, the *footing*, the topsoil is removed and a layer of concrete somewhat wider than the wall or pier which it is to support is placed on the ground (Fig. 10.14a). In poorer ground the individual footings under the walls of a building can be combined to form a single thicker and deeper *raft* foundation. Under a footing the pressure caused by the weight of the superstructure is dispersed into the soil beneath, and the advantage of a raft is that the pressure is spread into a much greater volume and depth of ground than

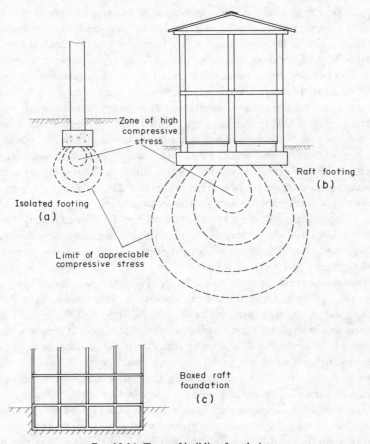

FIG. 10.14. Types of building foundation.

it is under a series of individual footings (Fig. 10.14b), and this reduces the settlement. The raft was developed by the Romans, who used their hydraulic concrete to place very heavy foundations of this type: the Red Basilica at Pergama in Turkey, for example, is on a raft several metres thick. Modern raft foundations gain their strength more from reinforcement than great thickness, and under large buildings are often constructed as a series of boxes in which the walls also serve as a basement (Fig. 10.14c).

In poorer ground still, *piles* consisting of tree trunks were used to support buildings at least as early as the Neolithic period, as we know from the remains of lake dwellings dating from this time in Central Europe. Ideally, piles are driven down until they strike rock, but even where this is not possible, as was usually the case in Roman and mediaeval foundations, a piled foundation spreads the superimposed load downwards and outwards into the ground much more effectively than is possible with a raft (Fig. 8.9c). Without the use of piles, cities like Venice and Amsterdam, located for strategic and economic reasons in marshes, could not have been developed at all. Piles were usually of carefully selected oak or, in the sea, greenheart from Central America. This was particularly resistant to the ravages of marine borers like *Teredo navalis*, which can destroy a piece of wood in a matter of months.

In the nineteenth century piles of steel and reinforced concrete were introduced and the techniques of placing them in position were greatly improved. One ingenious modern method is to drive a steel tube into the ground by dropping a heavy weight down inside it onto a plug of concrete or gravel at the bottom. Surprisingly, the plug is not forced out at the base but carries the tube down with it. When it has been driven far enough the tube is gradually withdrawn and filled at the same time with concrete and a cage of steel reinforcement, which remains in the ground as a pile. In Chicago the stiff clay made it possible to dig out shafts by hand up to 2 m in diameter and reaching down over 30 m into rock, and most of the skyscrapers in that city stand on concrete piers cast in such shafts; but it is seldom possible to work in the dry in this way. Nowadays large piles for bridge and building foundations are sunk by driving a steel tube into the ground with a backwards and forwards rotary motion, and removing the soil inside with a grab as the tube sinks. When the tube is down to position the water is pumped out and the bottom can be inspected and cleared up if necessary by sending men down; the inside is then filled with concrete, the tube being left in position. This technique, developed since 1945, enables piles 2 m in diameter and up to 60 m or more in length to be put in place.

The other technique for deep foundations, the *cofferdam*, remained more or less in the form developed by the Romans until the early part of the nineteenth century. The invention of the pneumatic caisson then enabled underwater foundations to be excavated under air pressure sufficient to keep the water out (Fig. 10.15). In really bad ground, in sand and silt particularly, it is necessary to excavate under compressed air, but pneumatic caissons are difficult and expensive to operate. The

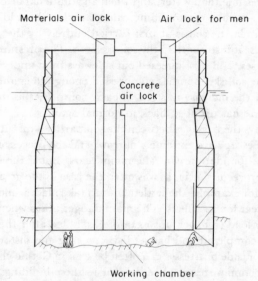

FIG. 10.15. Pneumatic caisson for Forth railway bridge.

workmen have to undergo a very slow "decompression" after a shift of work to avoid the dangerous "bends" or caisson disease. In any case, men cannot work efficiently in air pressures of more than 4 at-mospheres, and this limits the depth of compressed air caissons to about 35 to 40 m below water level. Wherever possible, caissons are open (that is, not under compressed air) and the ground is dredged out from inside by grabs; the water is finally pumped out and the bottom cleaned up for placing the concrete foundation of the pier.

Soil consists of a mass of solid particles of sand or clay or a mixture of both, more or less loosely packed and with the spaces or pores between the particles partly or wholly filled with water. As a result of the work of Terzaghi and others, the critical importance of the pore water is now understood. In soil lying undisturbed in the ground the weight of the earth above is carried by the solid particles (which are called the soil skeleton) and the water in the pores is at the normal pressure of water at that depth below the water table. The soil skeleton, however, is much more compressible than water, and when an additional load comes onto the ground—from a new building, for example—the additional compressive stress in the soil is at first carried entirely by the water in the pores, because it is stiffer than the soil skeleton. The pressure in the pore water increases, and it is squeezed out sideways from under the foundation until the soil skeleton has compressed enough to enable it to carry the whole of the increase in stress at each point. By this time the pore water pressure has dropped back to normal again.

In fine clays the passages between the soil particles through which the water has to escape are extremely narrow, and the process of consolidation under a foundation can take many years. But if the construction above also proceeds slowly, as was often the case in the great cathedrals of the past, for example, the settlement can take place while there is still time to correct for its effects. The main danger arises when some additional heavy load (a tower, for example) is added after the bulk of the structure is completed and has settled: cracking and distortion around towers and outside buttresses can often be seen in Gothic churches. The other very common result of settlement in these buildings is tilting of columns and outer walls caused by spread and rotation of the footings because the outward thrust of the roof produced uneven pressures under them.

But the most spectacular examples of foundation settlement have quite another cause. The pore water need not be squeezed out by pressure to cause consolidation. It can also be sucked out, as when boreholes are sunk into the ground and water is pumped out. This has happened in at least two notorious instances: Venice and Mexico City. The water supply of Venice originally came from the mainland, but from 1910 onwards this was increasingly supplemented from boreholes sunk to depths of up to 300 m in the clay under the city. The result has been a general subsidence of the buildings of Venice. Since the walls of most Venetian houses start only about a metre above average sea level, and damp courses were not incorporated in buildings until after 1800, even a settlement of 100 to 200 mm can be extremely damaging to the fabric of historic structures. Pumping has now been stopped and the settlement has been checked, but it cannot be reversed, and the future of the buildings of Venice is in grave doubt.

Mexico City is an even more spectacular and bizarre case. Much of the city is built on the soft bed, 30 to 40 m deep, of a dried-up lake which was drained over a period of three centuries. The buildings had reached stable levels and settlement was not a problem when, in the nineteenth century, pumping started from deep wells sunk to supplement the water supply. Today the ground level in the centre of the city is no less than 6 m lower than it was in 1900. Older buildings on shallow foundations have gone down with the general subsidence, some tilting drunkenly, and there has been endless trouble from cracked sewers, water pipes, and pavements. Modern multi-storey buildings on piled foundations have not settled, and they and the iron casings of wells stand up above the older structures, which go on sinking as pumping continues.

Pore water can also be removed from clayey soil by drying out in prolonged droughts such as occurred in the U.K. in the summer of 1976. Clay is a colloidal gel, and like other gels contracts when it loses water by, say, evaporation. It also contracts because of capillary pressure. If one end of a tube with a very fine internal diameter — the stem of an old thermometer will do for this — is put into water, the water is drawn up in the tube because of the phenomenon known as capillarity. The finer the bore of the tube the higher the water rises. Since it is held up above the level of the water outside, the tube must be put into compression. In clay the fine passages between the particles in the soil skeleton act like capillary tubes, and when the general ground-water level falls during dry weather the moisture in the clay is held by capillary action, and the soil is put into compressive stress which can amount in very fine clays to several atmospheres. The clay shrinks, causing seasonal settlements which in sensitive soils such as occur in parts of the cities of Melbourne and Adelaide in Australia, for example, can amount to as much as 100 mm; here house foundations have to be carried down below the depth of a metre or two to which volume changes extend, or alternatively the whole building must be based on a raft foundation which can move up and down bodily. Large trees will take up a thousand litres of water a day if they can get it, and species like poplar with extensive surface roots can be very damaging to buildings near them in times of drought;

houses on the London clay have suffered much from the accelerated drying out of the ground caused by near-by trees.

The greatest challenge to foundation designers today comes not on land but in the depths of the North Sea. In 1970 there suddenly arose a demand for fixed oil drilling and production platforms in water there up to 150 m deep. The latest of these huge structures are designed to rest on the sea bed under their own weight. The North Sea is notoriously rough, and the foundations are subjected to continually repeated variations of pressure from the pounding of waves on the superstructure. No one knows for certain how the soil under the sea bed will react in the course of time to this totally new kind of dynamic loading. Research is pressing on in tests on a much accelerated time scale, but the first gravity platforms are already in position. Yet another bold step into the unknown regions of structural engineering has been taken.

Some General Observations on Structural Action

Looking back over the preceding chapters, it may be worth while recapitulating and enlarging on a few basic truths about structural behaviour. Perhaps the most important point of all is that structures support loads in the most direct way open to them. We saw in the bowstring arch roof of Fig. 4.2b that if the shape of the curved arch member is right for the loads the forces pass directly through it to the supports, completely ignoring the web members. They take the most direct path available, provided it is suitably located. Another example is shown in Fig. 10.16: a load at the top of the triangular tower is

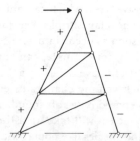

FIG. 10.16. Framed tower carrying load at apex.

transmitted straight down the two main members, and the inner bars are unstressed. The same is true of the building frame of Fig. 10.17a: the load applied at the top of the column goes directly down it to ground, and the rest of the structure is virtually unstressed. But if the

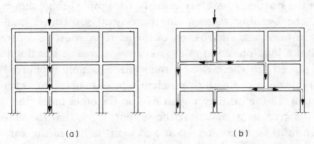

(a)   (b)

FIG. 10.17. Direct and indirect paths to ground in framed buildings.

direct path is interrupted, as at (b), a much more tortuous route has to be followed, and the stresses and deflections are greatly increased. The designer should always bear in mind this elementary yet basic rule: provide paths as simple and direct as possible for the loads to pass to the supports. The best structures have this characteristic: the members or elements are few and well disposed, their functions are obvious, and the whole effect inspires confidence. An ill-conceived structure, on the other hand, can arouse suspicion and unease even in the ordinary layman, as an amusing example given by Torroja in his book *The Philosophy of Structures* illustrates (Fig. 10.18).

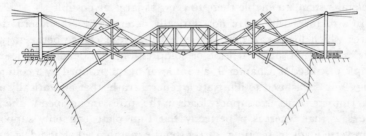

FIG. 10.18. Ahwillgate Bridge, India.

The larger the structure, the more important it is that the various parts should be arranged as efficiently as possible. Earlier in this chapter we saw how important this is in very tall buildings. Very large cantilever bridges are another example. Since in a very large bridge the predominant load is its own weight, this weight should be disposed so as to cause the smallest possible stresses. In the simple bridge shown in Fig. 10.19a, the bending moment in the central suspended span CD is greatest at midspan, and so most of the material must be concentrated there. But a load placed at midspan causes a greater bending moment than if placed anywhere else on the span. A simply supported beam, therefore, is not a particularly efficient type of structure for carrying its own weight. In the cantilever span BC, on the other hand, the bending moment is greatest at and near the support B, so that the material in this span must be concentrated at and near B. But in this case a load located near B produces only a small bending moment at B. The cantilever span BC, therefore, is a much better structure for supporting its own weight than the suspended beam span CD.

In very large cantilever bridges, therefore, the tendency is for the suspended span to become smaller and smaller in relation to the other spans. The Firth of Forth railway bridge (Fig. 10.19b) is a case in point. In some large-span European highway bridges this tendency has been carried to the limit, the suspended span being replaced by a hinge directly connecting adjoining cantilever arms (Fig. 10.19c). The weight of the largest dinosaurs was disposed in a way remarkably like the double cantilever spans of such bridges (Fig. 10.19d) and there is no doubt that in the process of evolution of these huge mammals their weight was gradually concentrated where it would cause the smallest forces in the skeletal system, to enable them to grow as large as possible.

In structures which are not statically determinate, the alternative paths which loads can take very often involve a choice between two modes of action, direct tension or compression, and bending. The example discussed in Chapter 9, a cantilever beam propped by a column (Fig. 9.6b), was used to illustrate a general truth, that all statically indeterminate structures support loads in the stiffest mode open to them. We saw that whereas a perfectly flat thin plate can only support transverse loads by bending, direct (tensile membrane) action develops as soon as it starts to deflect, and rapidly takes over from the bending

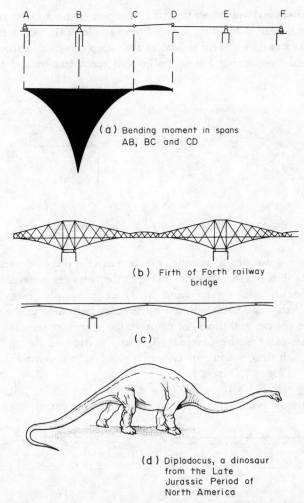

(a) Bending moment in spans
   AB, BC and CD

(b) Firth of Forth railway
     bridge

(c)

(d) Diplodocus, a dinosaur
    from the Late
    Jurassic Period of
    North America

FIG. 10.19. Disposition of stress-resisting material in very large cantilever structures.

action. This is an example of a structure assuming a stiffer mode of action as soon as its shape allows it to do so. The same reasoning, carried a little further, led us to conclude that thin shells support loads as far as possible by compressive membrane action rather than in bending.

Sometimes a simple alteration to a structure enables it to carry loads by direct instead of bending action. For example, if the portal frame of Fig. 10.20a carries a vertical load at the ridge, it acts as a fixed arch. The thrust line cannot follow the lines of the members and bending

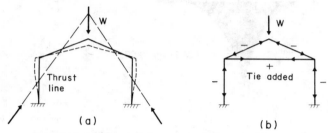

FIG. 10.20. Bending and direct action in factory portal frame.

stresses are set up which are much greater than the direct stresses due to the thrust. But if a tie is inserted between the two sides at eaves level, as at (b), the two inclined rafters and the tie act as a simple triangular roof truss, and the load is transmitted by direct compression in the rafters, tension in the tie, and finally by compression in the posts to the ground, with practically no bending at all. The insertion of the tie greatly reduces both stresses and deflections. We looked at a somewhat similar example in Fig. 10.8b and c.

During the 1930s the open-web or Vierendeel girder (Fig. 10.21) achieved some popularity as a form of steel bridge construction. From

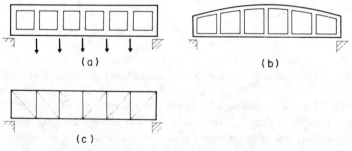

FIG. 10.21. Vierendeel or open-web girders.

our earlier discussion we can see at a glance that as pin-jointed frameworks such girders are deficient in members, because they lack diagonals. Such trusses consequently depend for their strength mainly on the bending resistance of the two chords considered independently, with some further strength which is gained from the verticals. But severe bending stresses are present even when the top chord is somewhat curved, and the joints must be made rigid, usually by welding. The simple addition of diagonal members, as at (c), transforms the behaviour of the structure. It is now able to act as a pin-jointed truss, in direct tension and compression, and will do so because this is a far stiffer mode of action than bending. There are sometimes circumstances where it is desirable for functional reasons to leave out the diagonals—this happens occasionally in buildings—but it is very rarely justified for bridges except on rather debatable aesthetic grounds.

Direct tension is, of course, preferable to direct compression, because of the danger of failure by instability in members and complete structures which are under compressive forces, and the need to add more material to avoid this. It is very rarely possible to avoid compression. Even in a predominantly tensile structure like a suspension bridge, the tensile forces in the cables must be balanced by compressive forces in the towers. But the skilful designer will minimize the loss of efficiency in compression by keeping the compressive members short, using a material (e.g. concrete) for them which requires lower stresses and therefore more stocky members less prone to instability, or by other means.

These examples also serve to explain why the members in steel triangulated trusses can be rigidly connected instead of being joined by frictionless pins, without affecting appreciably the magnitude of the axial forces assumed in the design of the members. Since a proper stable system of connected bars exists, the structure will support loads by direct action, whether the joints are frictionless or rigid, because this is a stiffer mode than bending. It is true that bending moments are induced in the members when the joints are rigid. These are caused by the fact that when the bars lengthen and shorten owing to the forces in them, the truss deflects. If the joints are pinned the angles between the members change very slightly, but if the joints are rigid this cannot happen, and the members are bent. These secondary bending effects alter only very slightly the direct forces in the bars. It is true that they do increase appreciably the maximum stresses in the members, but provided the steel is ductile these do not reduce the ultimate strength of the truss, which depends only on the direct tensile or compressive strength of each member. In fact, rigid connections increase the strength of the struts, for, as we can deduce from Fig. 7.10a and b, even a strut whose ends are only partially restrained against rotation by adjoining members will have a higher compressive strength than a pin-ended strut.

Another interesting general conclusion can be drawn from the simple structure of Fig. 9.6b. If the beam were made twice as deep, its stiffness would be increased eight-fold, and if the column retained its original dimensions the beam would attract roughly eight times as much of the load as before. It is a general principle that the addition of material to a part of a statically indeterminate structure will attract force to that part. For example, reinforced concrete members in frames are often haunched (i.e. deepened) near the corners, where the bending moments are greatest (Fig. 10.22). This has the effect of further increasing the

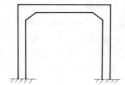

FIG. 10.22. Reinforced concrete portal frame with haunched members.

bending moments at these points, although the actual *stresses* are reduced because of the increased cross-section of the beam. Another example of this was discussed in Chapter 3 (Fig. 3.3b and c).

Thus in man-made structures, an increase in material at any point attracts force. In trees and other living structures, on the other hand, force attracts material: we noted in Chapter 6 that stress in bones and in the stalks of plants encourages growth and the accumulation of stress-resisting fibre. This is Nature's way of designing organic structures efficiently.

CHAPTER 11

Structural Design

THERE WAS a time when one and the same man would be responsible for the over-all conception, the detailed design, the construction, and even the continued maintenance, of a major bridge or building. Eiffel, Brunel, and the other giants of nineteenth-century structural engineering were complete designers in this sense. Nowadays such men are unfortunately rare: Nervi in Italy, or Arup in England are almost anachronisms in a world in which the division of labour has fragmented the design process among several distinct professions. But the good designer still bears in mind the total process of creating a structure when he sets to work. And he must have regard for the four criteria of good structural engineering that were enunciated in Chapter 1: *commodity*, or functional serviceability; *firmness*, or strength and safety; *delight*, or good appearance; and *economy*. Since he is a maker of structures, he is in one sense an artist; and if he is gifted his creations will carry the same indefinable stamp of inspired design that one feels in fine sculpture, pottery, or any of the other plastic arts.

These four criteria are not independent of each other, but (as we saw briefly in Chapter 1) interact in complicated ways in leading to the final form of a structural design. The primary criterion—the *raison d'être* of any structure, in fact—is commodity, its suitability for its intended function. It must work well, and do so for the term of its natural or intended life. In a building like an office block this means that the space should be adequate and well planned for the uses to which it is to be put, and the proper equipment must be provided. It must also be proof against the external environment—watertight, well lit, and well insulated thermally and acoustically. It is usually up to the architect and his other engineering consultants to see that the building works well in these respects. In a more strictly engineering structure like a bridge or dam, the structural engineer is much more in control of the functional criterion. He is responsible for the over-all layout and the detailed planning, and so also for the structural form. Commodity or functional serviceability must always be in the forefront of the designer's mind. A coal bunker, an oil-drilling platform, and an apartment building are all meant to do a particular job, and this must have a major influence on their general design and layout. The functional requirements of structures vary so much, however, that it would be impossible to go into a detailed discussion of them.

Firmness

How does the designer ensure that his structure will last for the whole of its intended life, hopefully without distress, and certainly without collapse? Let it be said at once that he never can be *quite* sure. He is in good professional company here. No one expects the surgeon to be successful every time he operates, any more than the criminal lawyer can guarantee to get his client off even if he is innocent. By the standards of other professions, however, the engineer is remarkably effective. Compared with the millions of structures which end their lives peacefully without ever having attracted attention by bad behaviour, those which fail in some way are very few. So rare, in fact, are failures of structures designed and built by professionally trained engineers that whenever one does occur it makes the headlines. The most disastrous, in material cost and in lives lost, have been collapses of dams; but even including these, the world-wide loss of life from failures of structures designed by engineers over the last two centuries can probably be counted in thousands, whereas the death toll on the roads since the invention of the motor car already runs into some millions. Ironically, the structural engineer has become the victim of his own professional efficiency. People take it for granted, and he gets no credit for it. But where, as in the Indian sub-continent and in South America, for instance, the design and construction of large apartment and office blocks have not always been under skilled engineering control, and building failures have been rather more common than elsewhere, it is significant that the structural engineer is highly regarded in the community!

Some uncertainty as to the strength of a particular structure, however, there must always be, and it is of two kinds. Firstly, there is doubt about the loads to which the structure will be subjected during its lifetime; and secondly there is the question of its ability to carry these loads safely.

Loads and Other Forces

In anticipating the different kinds of loads and forces likely to come onto the structure he is designing, the engineer has been helped since the turn of the twentieth century by design codes for the most common types of structure. But he must still use his judgement, and he can be caught napping, as we saw in Chapter 10 in the collapse of the Ronan Point apartment building. In hindsight, the possibility of an explosion should have been allowed for in the design; but it was not. Still more unfortunately for the designer, there may be an earthquake in a region where seismic movements were previously small or unknown. The unexpected cannot always be foreseen, and even when it is it may not be possible to guard against it except at unacceptable expense.

Loads are of two kinds: the weight of the structure itself, which is called the dead load, and the loads and other forces like wind pressure which it has to carry or resist from time to time, and which are called the live loads. Before the nineteenth century, most structures were massively built, and supported mainly their own weight. Even in the Gothic cathedrals, the most daring of earlier buildings, wind and other live loads were of minor significance compared with the dead load. This was because the materials used were weak and structural analysis was non-existent: in consequence, structures were extremely massive and heavy by modern standards.

In the design of a structure its weight has first to be estimated; once a preliminary design has been completed the actual weight can easily be calculated and the guess confirmed or corrected. Very rarely and quite inexcusably, this step is overlooked or mishandled in a major structure. In the ill-fated first Quebec railway bridge, it was found when all the detailed design had been done that the structure weighed 24 per cent more than had been assumed. The designer underestimated the additional stresses resulting from this, and went ahead with the design as it stood; without doubt this decision contributed to the disastrous collapse in 1907 of the largest span then attempted.

With the advent at the beginning of the nineteenth century of cast iron as a structural material in the beams and columns in buildings and in bridges, structures more slender and lighter, yet stronger, than anything seen before began to appear, and the effect of the live loads compared with that of the dead weight became more significant. This trend, which has continued ever since, is the main reason for the complexities, refinements, and difficulties of modern structural design.

Some kinds of live load can be calculated accurately—an example is the water pressure behind a dam, since the maximum depth of water is controlled by the overflow level and is known. But even here an unexpectedly heavy load can act, as in 1963 at the 260-m high thin-arched Vaiont dam in the Italian Alps, when a hillside slipped into the reservoir behind the dam and sent a wave of water 100 m high over the crest. Generally speaking, the longer the life of a structure the more likely it is that some time it will have to carry an unexpectedly heavy live load.

The case of wind loading illustrates this point. Until the latter half of the nineteenth century little concern seems to have been felt by designers for the effect of wind. The destructive force of hurricanes must have been obvious to an early engineer like Coulomb, who spent some years in Martinique, in the West Indies; but it would have been very difficult at that time to measure wind forces. Coulomb's contemporary, John Smeaton, who in 1759 had completed the first successful lighthouse on the Eddystone reef, off Plymouth, and whose judgement on the question of natural forces therefore carried much weight, took the view that in the worst "storm or tempest" wind pressures would not exceed 12 pounds per square foot, or about 575 N/m^2. We now know that at the site of his lighthouse they can be four times as great as he supposed.

The collapse of the Tay railway bridge in a storm in 1879 concentrated the minds of engineers wonderfully on the subject. While the bridge was being designed, its luckless engineer, Thomas Bouch, had consulted no less an authority than Sir George Airy, the Astronomer Royal, and was told in a jaunty letter that 10 pounds per square foot was all that was needed. (After the accident Sir George prudently revised this figure to 120 pounds per square foot!) On the strength of this advice Bouch, as he admitted at the enquiry into the disaster, apparently made "no special provision" for wind pressure on this very exposed structure.

Yet at the same time the figure used in the U.S.A. was 50 lb/ft^2, and in France 55. A few years later Sir Benjamin Baker assumed a wind pressure of 56 pounds per square foot in the design of the Firth of Forth railway bridge, a figure partly based on measurements he had made at the site, but undoubtedly influenced also by the Tay collapse, and not much in excess of what would be adopted today on the same site. At this time, however, each new major structural advance also meant a step into the unknown as regards wind pressure. When, at about the same date, Eiffel was designing the famous tower which bears his name, he could have had no knowledge of wind pressures at heights of up to 300 m above ground, for no one had ever been in a position to take the necessary measurements. In fact, he used the completed tower for such observations. Fortunately it proved strong enough for them to be taken.

Eiffel and Baker, and designers in general until quite recently, treated wind pressure as a steady, static force, like the pressure of water behind a dam. But a tall structure like the Empire State Building in New York does not merely deflect in the wind; it sways backwards and forwards about the average deflected position, sometimes by as much each way as the average deflection. This can only mean that the action of the wind is not steady, but dynamic. Since man began powered flight, and particularly in the last 30 years or so, a great deal has been learned about the wind. If clouds are filmed and the film is speeded up, they are seen to race along with a tumbling motion caused by the turbulent passage of the air. The wind at any point has an average speed and exerts an average pressure, but superimposed on this mean velocity it also acts in a series of gusts of higher speed, which buffet any obstacle in their path. These gusts are extremely variable in size and frequency, and the smallest (which are also the most frequent) exert the greatest additional pressure, and do most of the damage to roofs, windows, and projections like eaves. In the U.K. such details now have to be designed for the worst effects, those caused by the smallest gusts lasting on average 3 sec; buildings whose largest dimension is less than 50 m must be designed for the rather smaller effect (in terms of pressure) of 5-sec gusts; while in bigger buildings allowance must be made for 15-sec gusts, whose mean velocity is between 3 and 16 per cent less than that of 3-sec gusts, depending on the height and surroundings of the structure.

We also know much more than formerly about the variability of wind

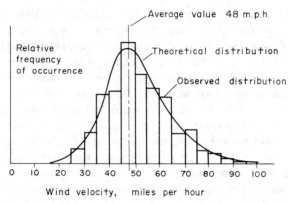

FIG. 11.1. Maximum wind speeds in New York over period 1884-1950.

speeds at a given place over a period of years. Plotted in Fig. 11.1 are records of the maximum speed measured over 5-min periods in each month between 1884 and 1950 in New York at a height of 140 m. From such a graph, which is known as a histogram, one can predict the likelihood of occurrence of a high wind of a particular speed over a period of, say, 50 years. The basic wind speed now recommended for structural design in the U.K. on the strength of similar records—it varies from 38 m/sec around London to 56 m/sec in the islands of the Outer Hebrides—is that which is likely to be exceeded, on average, only once in 50 years. This implies that in *any one year* there is a chance of 1 in 50 that it *will* be exceeded. Over a period of 50 years, however, it means statistically that there is a 1 in 1.6 chance that a stronger wind will blow. If the designer of a structure intended for a life of 50 years feels uneasy about this, and prefers, say, a 1 in 100 chance, then he must assume a basic wind speed 35 per cent greater. Since the pressure exerted by the wind is proportional to the square of the wind speed, his design wind pressure is stepped up by no less than 82 per cent—a decision which, taken one way, could easily double the cost of a tall building, or alternatively lose him and his firm a valuable competitive tender! Again, if he is happy about a risk of 1 in 50 in any one year, but wants to plan his structure for a 200-year life instead of a 50-year one, then he must allow for 21 per cent more wind pressure.

These points underline the hard fact that the engineer can never be absolutely sure that the wind pressure he designs his structure for will not be exceeded in its lifetime. He still cannot escape the responsibility of personal engineering judgement, even though it is based on much surer scientific data and statistical interpretation than was the case only 20 years ago. To be overcautious may lose him a commission; to take too much of a risk may lose him his reputation through the collapse of his structure.

What can happen when the laws of probability are ignored, and this is coupled with unsuspected weaknesses in the structural design of buildings, was vividly illustrated on Christmas Day 1974, when most of the coastal city of Darwin in Northern Australia was destroyed by cyclone Tracy. Darwin is in a region subject to severe cyclonic storms, but had not experienced a really bad one for 80 years. With a maximum wind speed of up to 70 m/sec Tracy cut a swathe of destruction into the coastal belt 20 to 30 km wide (which unluckily included the city) before it spent itself 50 km inland. The design wind speed officially recommended for buildings in Darwin was much too low—only 56 m/sec, the same as that for the Outer Hebrides—yet further down the same hurricane-prone coast at Onslow the figure was 70 m/sec. Nevertheless, buildings which had been properly designed for 56 m/sec winds stood up well. Unfortunately very few of the 8000 private houses in the city had been so designed (see Chapter 12) and more than half were totally destroyed. Luckily the death toll was only 50, but if Tracy had struck at high tide the storm surge could have flooded some of the city to a depth of 3 m and the loss of life must have been much greater. In hindsight it is clear that all buildings in Darwin should have been designed to withstand the full force of a severe cyclone, but such winds had not blown in living memory, and the public and even some professionals thought that they never would.

The action of wind on structures can be dynamic in another sense than that of buffeting by short-term gusts. When even a steady wind free from gusts flows past an obstacle like a tall chimney, a series of eddies or vortices are set up alternately at one side of the chimney and the other (Fig. 11.2a). Each vortex produces a drop in pressure at the side of the chimney, and this causes a sideways force first from one side and then the other. If the chimney is flexible and these alternating forces

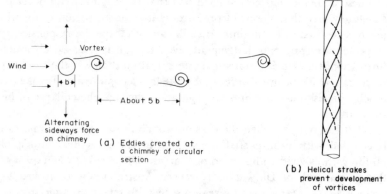

FIG. 11.2. Vortex excitation around chimney of circular section.

occur with a frequency which is very close to the natural frequency of the chimney, dangerously large forced vibrations can be set up. (Another example of forced vibration occurs when a child on a swing is given a slight push by its parents at each end of the swing's amplitude and it swings higher and higher.) The danger can be avoided by fixing spiral fins up the chimney: this prevents the vortices from developing (Fig. 11.2b). Similar in principle to this phenomenon, but much more damaging in its consequences, is the aerodynamic effect of wind on suspension bridges, which we will look at in Chapter 12.

We have still much to learn about the forces which large waves exert on structures. Even now the design of breakwaters exposed to heavy seas is to some extent a matter of guesswork. Perhaps the most remarkable instance in modern times of how engineers have been obliged to rely on intuition and trial and error occurred in the design of the early iron ships. In the 1850s the intrepid Brunel conceived the "Great Eastern", a wrought-iron vessel six times the size of any existing iron ship, a great box beam 211 m long, 25 m wide, and weighing 32,000 tonnes. This structure, colossal for its time, was intended to battle through the worst Atlantic gales, but its designer had no reliable information on the forces which a body of its size would encounter. It was designed as iron ships had been designed since the early 1800s, by simply assuming that as it rode a heavy sea the worst loading conditions would be when the hull was supported either at mid-length, on the crest of a wave, or at the ends, between successive waves, and that the height of the waves would be one-twentieth of the distance between them. That this was adequate for smaller ships had been proved by the fact that they made the Atlantic crossing without breaking up. But no one had any idea whether it would be a reasonable assumption for vessels of the size of the "Great Eastern" until the first measurements of the stresses in ships' hulls were made early in the present century. These showed, fortunately, that the traditional assumptions made by ship designers were if anything a little on the safe side, even for very large vessels, and calculations continue to be made on the same basis today.

One might suppose that, with the great expansion in our knowledge of natural forces, structural designers today would never have to venture so far into the unknown as did their Victorian and earlier predecessors. But new challenges will always appear, and the additional knowledge required for a new kind of structure is usually acquired only after the first pioneering prototype is built. The gravity type oil-drilling and production platforms in the North Sea, huge structures up to 175 m high and weighing several hundred thousand tonnes, are designed to be floated out into position and then to rest under their own weight on the sea bed. They have to withstand much greater forces than a ship in the same position, because they must remain stationary. They are being designed to resist the effect of waves about 30 m high and 350 to 450 m apart buffeting the platform at intervals of about 15 sec; but it is not known at present, when the designs for some have been completed and they are in position, how frequently such waves or even greater ones will occur, or what precisely are the forces which they exert on such obstructions. As we saw in Chapter 10, the design of the foundations as well as of the structure itself is in question. And the demand is already on the horizon for platforms in depths several times as great as the present maximum of about 150 m.

Compared with the force of the winds and the waves, the live loads in buildings due to furniture, stores, equipment, people, and so on are undramatic, almost static and far easier to predict. As in the case of wind forces, the smaller the area acted on, the greater the intensity of the loading. Any small area of floor in a multi-storey building may have on it a very heavy piece of furniture like a piano or a set of filing cabinets, and if the stresses in the parts of the structure (floor beams, for instance) near such load are directly affected by it, they must be designed for these concentrated effects. But the complete floor area of a storey of the building (unless perhaps it is a warehouse) is most unlikely to be so heavily loaded at any one time. And so, in designing the columns which support the floors, it became the practice in U.S. skyscrapers, even before the turn of the twentieth century, to reduce the design loads on the floors: for example, 100 per cent of the design load on the top floor, only 95 per cent on the next floor down, 90 per cent on the next, and so on in steps of 5 per cent reduction per floor to a minimum of perhaps 50 per cent. This practice was based purely on engineering judgement, and it was not until the 1930s that actual measurements of the loads in buildings confirmed the intuitive guesses and, in fact, showed them to be on the safe side.

In bridges, too, there is a similar dependence of the intensity of loading on the size of the structure. If the bridge consists, say, of two main girders joined together at intervals by cross girders on which the roadway is supported, each cross girder will have to carry the heaviest axle load which passes over the bridge. But the bridge as a whole is most unlikely to be crowded with a closely packed train of such vehicles, and the longer the bridge the more improbable this contingency is. It has therefore become the practice to design highway bridges for a combination of a heavy concentrated load on each traffic lane (which ensures that secondary members like cross girders will be strong enough) together with a distributed load which is spread uniformly over the bridge, and whose intensity diminishes rapidly as the loaded length increases. The main members of very large bridges, therefore, are designed for a much smaller intensity of live load than short ones.

Of all the forces which structures may have to carry, those caused by earthquakes are the most destructive and unpredictable. Fortunately, severe seismic shocks are confined to fairly well-defined regions of the earth; but within these zones a particular place may not suffer a major earthquake for hundreds of years and then be completely destroyed by one. Anybody who has experienced a severe earthquake has felt the violent jerking of the ground to and fro as the shock waves pass, and heard their terrifying roar. The effect on a building or other structure is that it is subjected to a sudden horizontal acceleration, and it has been the practice to allow for this by designing the structure to carry a certain fraction of its weight applied as a horizontal static force. In strongly seismic regions the fraction is taken as about one-tenth. The forces involved can be enormous, as much as ten times as great as the force due to wind, which, as we have already seen in Chapter 10, otherwise constitutes the dominant loading in tall buildings.

If one holds a flexible cane or lath vertically and agitates it rapidly backwards and forwards, one gets some idea of what happens to a tall building or other flexible structure during an earthquake. Depending on its flexibility and natural period of vibration, parts of the building may at any moment be moving in the same direction as the seismic acceleration or against it. Nowadays it is realized that the old, crude, static methods of earthquake design may be too conservative or unsafe, depending on the type of structure, and that the *dynamic* response of the structure must be considered. (The same approach is now followed in analysing the buffeting effect of wind gusts on tall, flexible buildings like the World Trade Center in New York, not so much from the expectation of collapse as to make sure that the occupants are not bothered by excessive vibration.)

Rough and ready though the old rules are, however, buildings designed in this way have generally stood up well in earthquakes. Most of the material damage and loss of life has followed the collapse of buildings not so designed. Unfortunately, many of the earthquake-prone regions of the world are poor countries where housing is too flimsy to stand up even in moderate disturbances, and there is little prospect that this situation will improve for many years. People's memories, too, are short — it is the Darwin story again — and 50 years of quiescence can convince individuals and even governments that the seismic danger has passed for ever. But even 500 years is a very short period in geological time, and until we know much more about earthquakes all we can say is that in a region known to have been seismically active in the historical past there is always some risk. It is a matter of chance of a kind which cannot, unfortunately, be estimated statistically.

Earthquakes are an extreme example of dynamic loading, but most live loads come on to the structure fairly suddenly. If we place a 1-kg weight very gently on the pan of a spring balance it will record, as we would expect, a reading of 1 kg. But if it is held above the pan and just touching it, and then is suddenly released, the scale will go down momentarily to a maximum reading of about 2 kg and oscillate before coming to rest at 1 kg. And if the weight is held some distance above the pan and dropped onto it, the maximum reading temporarily recorded will be even greater than 2 kg. Similarly, a road vehicle running quickly onto a short bridge produces a maximum stress in the structure greater than that caused when it is stationary at midspan. This fact was well known to the early railway engineers, and they doubled the static stress set up by the passage of a locomotive. Recent research, however, has shown that in a typical steel bridge the stresses are much less than doubled; the impact allowance by which the weight of the vehicle is increased is usually about 0.3 or less.

Dynamic loads, however, introduce other hazards. If the steel in a structure is brittle the shock of a suddenly applied load may cause fracture. Even if it is quite ductile, moderate live loads repeated thousands or millions of times can bring about failure by fatigue. And we have already seen how in suspension bridges a flexible response to repeated loads can cause a build-up of deflection to such a pitch that the structure is destroyed. But these are matters which we must leave until Chapter 12.

To conclude this discussion on the loads to which structures are subjected, we can say that while dead load—the weight of the structure—can be calculated with accuracy, the various kinds of live load which act on it from time to time, cannot. We can never be absolutely sure that an exceptionally and unexpectedly heavy live load—a great wind, an overloaded lorry, in the case of a long bridge an unprecedentedly concentrated line of heavy vehicles—will not act on it at some time or other. We know enough now about wind to be able to predict the probability of occurrence of very severe gales; for other kinds of live load, unfortunately, we cannot yet say as much, though we know that in general the histogram of frequency of occurrence looks something like Fig. 11.1. Combining, then, the dead and live loads we can draw a diagram like Fig. 11.3 to represent the history of loading on the structure.

Strength

The capacity of structures to support the expected loads without distress—alarming deflections, cracking, permanent set when the loads

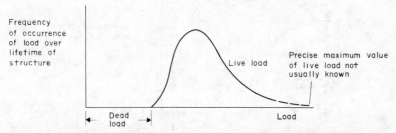

Fig. 11.3. Diagram to illustrate history of loading on a structure.

are removed—or, in the last resort, collapse, is far more predictable than it was 50 years ago; but the strength of a particular structure still cannot be predicted with absolute confidence. In the first place, structural materials, whether natural or man-made, vary in quality and

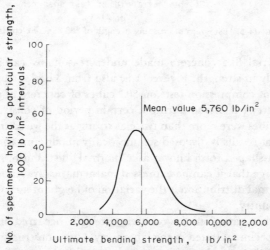

Fig. 11.4. Histogram of bending strength of 1373 samples of Sitka spruce.

strength. Figure 11.4, for example, shows a graph given by Pugsley of the variability of the bending strength of 1373 small specimens of Sitka spruce used in earlier types of aircraft. The range of strength is extremely wide—from about 22 N/mm² to about 65 N/mm². Even a manufac-

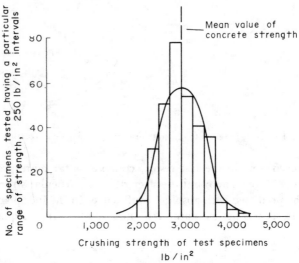

FIG. 11.5. Histogram of crushing strength of 303 concrete cubes.

tured material like concrete made under reasonably careful control varies widely in strength. Figure 11.5, also from Pugsley's book, shows the results of compression tests on 303 cubes of concrete of supposedly the same strength, made during a certain period of construction: the strongest cubes were more than twice as strong as the weakest. This particular set of results is disposed symmetrically about a mean value, and takes a bell-shaped form known as a "normal" distribution, which has the advantage that it can be expressed mathematically. Another example of a normal distribution is the variation of height of men of a certain age in a country.

These wide variations in concrete strength occurred in carefully prepared specimens tested in the laboratory. On a construction site concrete cannot be placed with the same care as this. It is possible if supervision is very lax for it to be tipped in and left to flow around the reinforcing steel without the thorough compaction and vibration which produces a dense, strong concrete of uniform quality. Test cylinders drilled from the hardened concrete would then show much greater variation in strength than the specimens taken during the mixing process, as well as a lower *average* strength.

Again, the strength of reinforced concrete construction depends critically on accurate location of the steel bars in the work. If not properly supported and secured they can be displaced slightly and the strength of a thin slab, for example, can easily be 25 per cent weaker than intended. (Cantilevered balconies in apartment buildings have been known to collapse because the steel bars were placed near the bottom of the slab instead of the top, or even left out entirely, but this kind of gross error can never be guarded against by a greater margin of safety.) Again, steel joists and other sections are rolled under very careful control, but some variation in thickness and depth cannot be avoided, and this affects their strength. Concrete form work may be slightly out in dimensions; load-bearing walls in a multi-storey building may be out of alignment one above the other; the welding techniques used in a steel bridge may be defective; these and many other possible defects in construction can affect the strength of the finished structure.

Age and atmospheric conditions can affect some structural materials, especially if the structure is poorly maintained. If timber members become wet through condensation or leakage of rain water, they lose some strength, and more than one plywood box beam roof in the U.K. has collapsed for this reason. In the early 1970s collapses of several school assembly halls, swimming pools, and gymnasia revealed that the special high alumina cement concrete in the roof beams (this cement sets hard in 24 hours and so enables construction to be speeded up) had lost most of its strength because of a chemical change (called "conversion") in the cement paste resulting from a combination of high temperature and high humidity. More recently still, calcium chloride added to concrete mixes to make them set more quickly has been found to cause corrosion of steel reinforcement and, in consequence, failure of some school buildings in the U.K. and of prestressed concrete pipes in Canada. As in the case of DDT and thalidomide in the public health field, the hidden dangers associated with substances used for their immediately beneficial properties did not emerge until too late.

Another cause of uncertainty about structural strength lies in the limitations, even today, of structural analysis. The first scientifically calculated assessment of the ultimate strength of a structure (that of the dome of St. Peter's Cathedral in Rome) dates only from 1748. Earlier designers had to depend on the hazardous approach of trial and error, supplemented perhaps with experiments on crude models.

Prudent engineers of the early nineteenth century like Telford, Brunel, and Stephenson relied heavily on the testing of large and expensive scale models, as well as on the methods of analysis of elastic stresses in various kinds of structure which were then available. In the century between 1850 and 1950 structural engineers came to depend more and more on their ability to calculate the stresses set up by the ordinary working loads on the structure, and the aim was to keep these "elastic" stresses well below the limit of proportionality or elastic limit of the material used. The testing of models to destruction went out of fashion, and the realistic assessment of ultimate strength was rather lost sight of.

More recently, as we have seen earlier, it has been realized that while elastic analyses give a good idea of the behaviour of structures under the loads expected in service—in particular, the deflections and the likelihood of cracking and other signs of distress—they are not a good guide to ultimate strength, because of the redistribution of internal forces which takes place once yielding occurs, except in truly statically determinate structures. Ultimate strength analysis has been well developed for some types of structure, but cannot be expected to give a very precise prediction of strength even for these. It cannot be applied at all with any confidence to highly redundant classes of structure like thin concrete shell roofs or the most recent types of multi-storey buildings with load-bearing walls or core or tube systems.

Because of all these grounds for uncertainty in the prediction of structural strength, if, say, 100 bridges of a particular type and size were designed and built for a given loading, and tested to destruction, the strengths would inevitably vary somewhat about a mean value (Fig. 11.6). For many kinds of structure the average strength can now be predicted with some assurance—say, to within plus or minus 10 per cent—but the shape of the strength histogram and the minimum likely value are less certain.

Relation between Loads and Strength

If the loads on a structure are under very strict control, and it is of a type whose strength can be closely estimated and it is built and main-

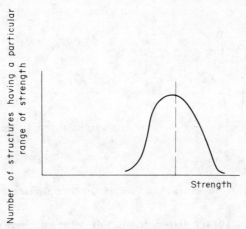

FIG. 11.6. Diagram to illustrate variation of strength of a number of supposedly identical structures.

tained under strict supervision, the variation in loading L and strength S will be very small, and the two histograms might look like those shown in Fig. 11.7a. Evidently the average strength S_a need then be only a little greater than the average intensity of load L_a for the structure to be quite free from danger of collapse. The ratio of S_a to L_a (which is known as the ultimate load factor) could safely be fixed at little more than unity. But this is an ideal situation. As a rule, loading and strength vary much more widely, and the upper tail of the load histogram overlaps the lower tail of the strength histogram, as in Fig. 11.7b, unless S_a is made a good deal bigger than L_a. In other words, unless we provide a reasonably large load factor there is some small possibility that at some time an exceptionally heavy load will prove too much for the structure, and it will collapse. Putting more strength into it will put up its cost, and a balance has to be struck between a completely safe but very expensive structure and a less expensive one in which the risk of failure is not completely absent.

But, assuming that enough is known of the characteristics of loading and strength to enable the designer to calculate probabilities of failure, on what basis should he decide on the level of probability? One approach is through the protection of the public from fatal accidents

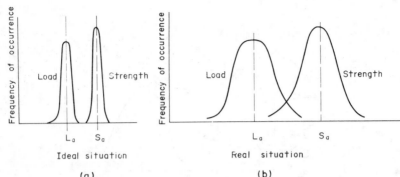

Ideal situation   Real situation

(a)   (b)

Fig. 11.7. Histograms of load and strength for a particular structure.

caused by structural collapse. In aircraft, where the user is always more conscious of the possibility of failure than in earthbound structures, Pugsley has mentioned the tendency to regard a fatal accident rate of less than 1 in 10 million flying hours as "acceptable".

Since the loads to which aircraft are subjected in flight have been carefully recorded, and the strength of particular models is known within close limits because of the refinements of the design process and the extensive prototype testing that precedes production of a new design of aircraft, it is indeed possible to arrive at an ultimate load factor on the basis of a certain probability of failure during a given planned life. On the French State Railways over a number of years there was roughly one death for every million travelling hours, and this seemed to be acceptable to the public. On British roads the death-rate from vehicular accidents is roughly 1 in 10,000 of the population per annum, which means, on the assumption that each person in the country travels on average for 300 hours each year, a death-rate of 3 in 10 million travelling hours — a figure which the public, though not exactly happy about, still seems to put up with. The trouble with applying this approach to the calculation of safety margins in structural design is that, as was mentioned at the beginning of this chapter, in the last 200 years only some thousands of deaths have resulted from structural failures for which professional engineers were responsible. Furthermore, most failures occur during construction and are not usually a hazard to the general public but only to one section of it, the people engaged on the construction. The probability of death from a structural accident, measured in the incidence in terms of the number of hours spent by the individuals in the community on or near structures must, therefore, be infinitesimally small compared with the rates for aircraft, railways, and road vehicles. The public gets, and therefore takes for granted and expects, a far higher degree of safety in buildings, bridges, and other structures than it is willing to tolerate in moving vehicles. The chance of death is so very small, in fact, that without much more accurate data on loads and strength than engineers now possess it would be impossible to assess load factors on this basis.

Another approach is in terms of the cost of replacing a collapsed structure. A water tower, let us say, has to be provided for a small community. Should it be built as cheaply as possible, with a minimum margin of safety and, therefore, a high probability of failure at some time? Or would it be better to make it less liable to fail, which would cost more initially? A failure would mean additional cost in repairs or reconstruction as well as in keeping the water supply going during the work. A designer with enough experience of how the cost of such structures varies with the factor of safety could work out how much money should be spent on the tower initially to keep the first cost plus the probable cost of a failure (the capitalized cost of this times the probability of failure) to a minimum. Where people might be injured or killed in such an accident it should be possible (as is now done in the aircraft industry) to include the probable cost of insurance claims.

Failure in the case of a water tower does not necessarily mean a spectacular collapse: if it leaks and has to be shut down for repairs this is a failure too. Indeed, not only must a structure be safe under an accidental overload; under the normal working loads its functioning must not be impaired by cracking, alarmingly large deflections or vibrations, permanent set, or other signs of distress. Collapse due to overload and malfunctioning under the working load were both contingencies of which the early structural designers in wrought iron were very conscious. The first could be guarded against by testing models or full-scale prototypes to destruction, the second by keeping the design stresses well below the elastic limit of the iron. The first official step in this direction was taken by the Board of Trade in the U.K. in the 1840s when it fixed the stress in wrought-iron bridges under the working loads to 5 tons/in^2, about half of the elastic limit. Since this also meant a figure of less than a quarter of the ultimate strength of the material, it came to be regarded as implying also a factor of four or more against failure. By the turn of the century this philosophy of structural safety was so generally accepted that when the first London County Council rules for the use of steel in building construction came to be drawn up, the working stress specified (7.5 tons/in^2) was, inevitably, a quarter of the average ultimate tensile strength of the steel then available.

In the following 50 years, as accumulated experience demonstrated that the working stresses used led to safe structures, the "stress" factor of safety laid down by codes for the design of steel structures crept down to about 3. The real margin of safety in statically indeterminate structures was known to be greater than this; but it was not until after the Second World War that enough research had been done to enable "collapse" methods of design to be recommended with confidence in building codes. In steel construction, where these developments have gone furthest, the engineer now has the option of either the traditional "elastic" method or of designing his structure to collapse at about 1.75 times the ordinary working loads, which enables him without any sacrifice in real safety margins to save as much as 20 per cent of the steel required. In concrete structural design, also, there is now a choice between methods based on working stresses and on ultimate strength.

The irony is that in some important details of design engineers have always used the collapse philosophy without realizing it. They assume, for example, that the bolts or rivets in a joint in a compression or tension member share the load in the member equally. But this is true only at the point of failure, and sometimes not even then in very big joints in major bridges; under the working loads some rivets are very highly stressed, others hardly at all. Until the last 50 years or so, the extent of these very serious stress concentrations was not realized, and without any information on the actual strength of large bridge joints (since they are too strong to be broken in any existing testing machine) engineers assumed, in effect, that the stress concentrations did not exist. Their reputations, and the bridges they built, were saved by the ductility of the steel, which enabled the stress concentrations to be ironed out in most cases before the joint failed. But it is certain that the strength of the largest tension joints falls below what is assumed in design by as much as 40 per cent. Fortunately, this is covered by the load factor (the factor of ignorance, as some engineers disarmingly call it) and by the fact that in large bridges the live load is so much smaller than the dead weight that an accidental overload is unlikely to cause much additional stress in the joints.

One feature of earlier building codes has been carried over into the collapse approach. If a building was designed to carry the gravity loads (the dead load and the live loads on the floors) and the additional stresses caused by wind were then calculated, the designer was not required to strengthen his building if the additional stresses were not more than, typically, 25 per cent of the gravity load stresses. The collapse load factor where wind is involved in this way conforms to this philosophy and is about 1.40, or 25 per cent less than 1.75. This is cutting things very fine, especially as the original basis for it—the low probability, presumably, that the wind provided for in the code would blow while the building carried its full gravity load—is obviously suspect. It has no qualitative statistical justification, at least, and its use in the design of very large and important buildings ought to cause concern, especially as much of the hidden reserve of strength in steel-framed buildings once provided by encasing the beams and columns in concrete (to protect them from fire) has disappeared with the introduction of light-weight fire protection.

Structural design is now at a turning-point. Engineers are aware that safety is relative, never absolute; that it depends on the variability of loads and strength; that the latter is affected by gaps in the designer's analytical armoury; that the margin of safety provided should vary with the importance of the structure and with the seriousness of collapse, in human and in economic terms; and that it should depend on whether failure, when it comes, is abrupt, as in statically determinate structures, or whether the structure gives prior notice, by distress or a partial failure in a non-critical part, that it is being overtaxed (what is called in the aircraft industry "fail-safe" design). The process of quantifying this philosophy in logical load factors for different types of structure is far from complete, but a start has been made. Because so few structures designed by engineers fail in service, there is always a powerful drive towards lower margins of safety and the cheaper structures which result; but it can now be conducted on a surer basis than hitherto.

A good deal of theoretical work has been done on the assumption that the load and strength curves in Fig. 11.7b are normal distributions. But a "normal" distribution is rather abnormal in Nature; and the answer one gets depends critically on the exact shapes of the intersecting tails of the two curves, even if their over-all shapes do approximate to normal distributions. As Sir Alexander Merrison, the chairman of the British committee which reported in 1973 on the design of steel box girder bridges, has said: "Although one's attitude to load factors must be shaped by a thorough-going analysis of the many parameters which go into them, in the end there is no escaping the use of sound engineering judgement about what is safe and what is not safe."

Perhaps the most useful attempt at determining load factors made so far, by a committee of the Institution of Structural Engineers in 1955, relies very much on engineering judgement. Load factors for a particular structure were assessed by the use of two groups of parameters, those affecting the probability of collapse (materials, workmanship, inspection, and maintenance; loading, including the degree of control over the loads; and the accuracy with which strength can be estimated) and those influencing the seriousness of a collapse (danger to personnel; and the cost of a failure). Numerical values based on extensive engineering experience were assigned to the five factors mentioned and then combined to give an ultimate load factor. The process is admittedly empirical and pragmatic but it does compel the designer to think seriously about the most important considerations behind structural safety.

Finally, the fact that a properly designed structure must be well behaved under the working loads as well as sufficiently strong to withstand overloading safely has been formalized in recent years by what is known as the "limit state" approach to design, in which these two limiting situations are recognized and included in the design process.

Delight

With rare exceptions, structures are built to fulfil useful functions, not to create works of art. Nevertheless, the designer of any structure which can be seen has an obligation to the public to try to make it pleasing to the eye. Here he is no longer on the fairly sure ground of structural calculations. The long and arduous training required of a structural engineer can stultify the aesthetic senses, but this is not the main difficulty. For there are no fixed, permanently accepted canons of good taste in structural appearance.

Fashions change in the visual aspects of structure just as completely as in clothing, if more slowly. William Morris was disgusted by the Firth of Forth railway bridge, regarding it as "the supremest specimen of all ugliness", and Guy de Maupassant is said to have fled in horror at first sight of the Eiffel Tower; yet neither of these structures seems to offend aesthetes today. Indeed, were the French Government to decide that the Tower must go, there would undoubtedly be a public outcry, and probably a political crisis. On the other hand, the embellishments on some of the bridges and other structures erected during the Gothic Revival of the last century, however acceptable they were then, now merely repel many people. Although superfluous ornament will undoubtedly become popular again in time, there is today a disdain for unnecessary architectural window-dressing and a liking for simple, clean lines.

It is only a short step from this to the view that if the pure structural form is displayed simply and truthfully, the visual effect is bound to be pleasing. Very occasionally, as in the Olympic Swimming Pool in Melbourne, Australia (Fig. 8.10), this does happen. But truth, as Oscar Wilde remarked, is rarely pure and never simple. The human form at its best is beautiful: the hidden skeleton with its accompanying muscles, tendons, and ligaments, structurally efficient though it may be, is not attractive. Essays in structural functionalism, as this philosophical attitude is called, do not always come off, and the bigger the structure the riskier the experiment is (see, for example, Fig. 10.12). To take one instance, for a fixed-ended concrete arch carrying a uniformly distributed load to be equally stressed at all cross-sections, the rib width may need to vary as shown in Fig. 11.8a; if the load is transmitted to the rib through piers (Fig. 11.8b) there should ideally be a kink in the arch axis at each pier. But structural functionalism is never carried to such lengths even in the largest arch spans, where economy in material is so important: a smooth curved shape which pleases the eye is worth the extra cost (see the Gladesville Bridge, Fig. 3.18, for example). It may not necessarily be more expensive, however, for the cost of the supporting formwork in the case of Fig. 11.8a would be higher than if the rib were of uniform thickness. Again, for maximum economy in material a two-

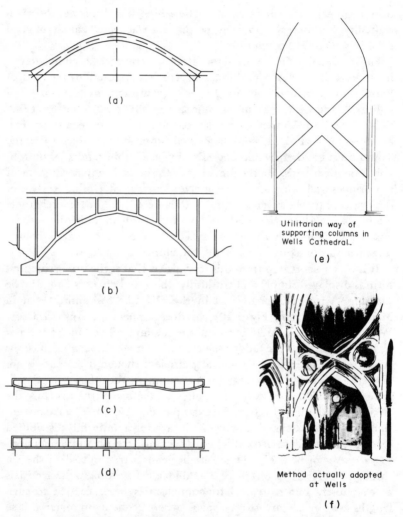

(a)

(b)

(c)

(d)

Utilitarian way of supporting columns in Wells Cathedral..

(e)

Method actually adopted at Wells

(f)

Fig. 11.8. Structural functionalism and good appearance.

span continuous steel girder bridge should vary in depth somewhat as shown in Fig. 11.8c, but some economy in material is usually sacrificed nowadays, especially in small spans, to give the simpler, cleaner lines of

Fig. 11.8d (in any case, increased fabrication costs in Fig. 11.8c probably outweigh the saving in steel). In Wells Cathedral in England, settlement of the foundations in mediaeval times made it necessary to provide bracing between the columns supporting the tower. Straight stone
struts (Fig. 11.8e) would have been the simplest and most efficient way
of doing this, but they would have clashed visually with the Gothic arches and vertical columns of the building, and the more expensive solution of Fig. 11.8f was adopted instead.

The designer with a feeling for good appearance knows how to
modify purely structural elements to give them visual beauty. In the
temples of ancient Greece — the Parthenon, for example — the proportions of the gabled ends were modified very slightly to improve the visual
impression of stability: the columns bulge towards mid-height and are
inclined inwards at the top, and the column spacing is decreased
towards the sides, but these and other refinements are so very slight as to
be imperceptible, except in the general impression created. Bridge piers
supporting large continuous girder spans are often made thicker than
they need be for purely structural reasons, because of a feeling by the
designer that they will not look strong enough to support the superstructure, and be out of proportion for this reason.

At the same time, a deliberate attempt to conceal the real structural
form by giving it some quite different external appearance always
offends the trained observer, although the ordinary layman may not be
aware of the deception. The present Waterloo Bridge in London, completed in 1942, replaced an earlier multiple-arched bridge, and looks
like one itself. But it is in fact a series of reinforced concrete beam spans
with façades shaped to look like arches. To compound the deception,
the façades, also in reinforced concrete, have grooves which give the appearance of joints between stone voussoirs; and, to make matters still
worse, these joints are vertical even though in a genuine stone-arched
bridge they would be set at right angles to the axis of the arch and be
vertical only at the crown. The urge to dress the structure up to look like
something else is sometimes carried to quite ludicrous lengths, as in
Telford's design (fortunately not adopted) for the Clifton suspension
bridge, in which the suspension chains appeared to hang from delicate
stone Gothic towers which could obviously never have supported them.

Errors like this often arise from the innate conservatism of human beings, their reluctance to abandon established practices, and their antagonism towards new, unfamiliar things. At the first performance of Stravinsky's *Rite of Spring*, a milestone in musical history, the novelty of the music nearly caused a riot. Not surprisingly, the earliest motor cars looked remarkably like horse-drawn carriages; the driver's seat was raised so that he could see over the non-existent horse, and there was even a little tube in which to place the hypothetical whip when not in use. In the case of Waterloo Bridge, anything other than an arched bridge, in appearance at least, on the site of a famous arched bridge was evidently unthinkable, even though the ground there is not firm enough for economical arched construction. Torroja points out that although a flagpole has to resist considerably heavier forces at its base than a lamp-post of the same height, lamp posts (until recently, at least) were expected to look solid and stocky and flagpoles very slender. Such conventional attitudes have origins which are buried in man's experience.

It is not enough, evidently, for a structure to *be* safe; to be aesthetically satisfactory it must also *look* safe. Telford's design for the Clifton Bridge violated this rule, as did the Indian bridge illustrated earlier (Fig. 10.18). Sometimes, however, appearances are deceptive. When the first concrete cylindrical shell roofs were built, even some structural engineers could not understand why the arched vault was not supported along the sides to resist the lateral thrust of the arch (Fig. 11.9); whereas in fact the roof acts longitudinally, as a beam, and will not perform properly if it is supported laterally.

No support here ?

FIG. 11.9. Lack of lateral support in cylindrical shell roofs.

There are, of course, well-established rules of architectural composition. Many famous buildings have been proportioned on the basis of the golden section (Fig. 11.10a); and unresolved duality, in which a

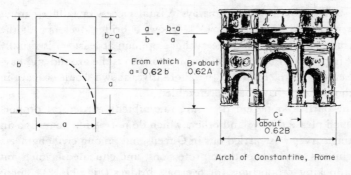

Arch of Constantine, Rome

Golden section
(a)

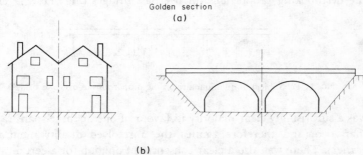

(b)

FIG. 11.10. Golden section and unresolved duality.

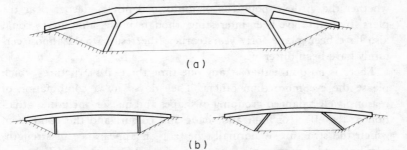

(a)

(b)

FIG. 11.11. Aesthetics of overpass bridges.

building or other structure is divided centrally into two equal parts (Fig. 11.10b), is often considered undesirable because the two equal masses compete with one another. Yet many good-looking bridges with central piers have been built over motorways. Visual success or failure cannot be determined so simply. Fig. 11.11 shows a bridge over one of the British motorways which, in the author's opinion at least, fails visually because it gives the impression of wishing to rise off the ground and having to be held down. Either of the alternatives shown would—again in the author's view—have been preferable.

At any particular period there are undoubtedly structural proportions which please the eye and others which do not. A few years ago an interesting survey was carried out in Queensland among civil engineers and architects, students of these professions, and educated laymen, on the best-looking proportions for overpass bridges (Fig. 11.12). There

FIG. 11.12. Subject of questionnaire on the proportions of overpass bridges.

was a surprisingly clear majority in favour of one or three spans rather than two (and therefore against the unresolved duality mentioned earlier). There was also a clear consensus of opinion for a certain ratio of pier thickness to girder depth, and of girder depth to span, as to whether the girders should be level or cambered, and by how much, and whether the girders should be of uniform depth or deeper near the piers. It would have been interesting, though, if the same survey could also have been made forty years earlier: the result would almost certainly have been different.

There is no doubt that at any one time there are structures which please the eye more than others. They do so for a combination of reasons: well-balanced grouping of shapes and masses, including attention to the effect of light and shade and colour, and the point from which the structure is normally viewed; an appearance of strength, stability, and a reasonable (but not too great) impression of lightness; structural honesty and functionalism, so long as it is not overdone; clean lines and (at present) an absence of unnecessary embellishment; and an obvious fitness for the intended purpose. But the attitude of each observer is also conditioned by his cultural background and personal tastes: beauty is indeed in the eye of the beholder.

The Task of the Designer

The structural designer must obviously make sure that his structure does its job well, that it fulfils its function, otherwise his client will soon complain. It must show no signs of distress in service and must also have a reasonable margin of strength against accidental overload or unexpected kinds of loading. It must look presentable. And it must be reasonably economical.

This last criterion, cost, is relative, like the others. If we are ill we do not look for the cheapest doctor; and in structural engineering the cheapest solution is not necessarily or usually the best. Until post-mediaeval times, cost was not an important factor in structural engineering: a pyramid or cathedral had to be built, and the labour and materials were somehow forthcoming. There was also very little choice of materials or structural form. In Roman days a solution to the problem of carrying a highway across a river was virtually limited to a series of stone and concrete piers connected either by semi-circular stone arches of spans not greater than about 30 m, or by timber arches or trusses. There were no structural calculations: the proportions of the spans were based on experience and on trial and error. The structural achievements of the Romans depended mainly on their constructional and organizational genius, on their intuitive grasp of structural principles, and on their invention of hydraulic cement. Cost was not an important consideration in a civilization largely based on slave labour.

Another important feature of structural engineering until well into the nineteenth century was that the designer was also responsible for the construction of the work. The two giants of Victorian structural engineering—Isambard Kingdom Brunel and Robert Stephenson—had a complete grasp of constructional techniques and personally directed the construction of their masterpieces. Their designs naturally took fully into account, and were greatly influenced by, the fabrication and erection methods used to put the structures together. Brunel, especially, used with unerring skill and a sensitive regard for their different properties and characteristics all the materials then available—stone, brick, concrete, timber, cast iron, and wrought iron. By then, too, structural design was already a highly skilled art. The designer had to have a general knowledge of the new methods of analysis of a variety of structural types—cables, arches, continuous beams, and trussed frameworks in particular. Cast iron, with its high compressive strength but its weakness in tension, had already presented the designer with new problems; but the really great challenge came with the mass production, from the early years of the nineteenth century onwards, of wrought iron, the first ductile material with really good tensile properties. Much greater spans suddenly became feasible, not only in chain suspension bridges but also in the new structural forms — beams and trusses, especially — made possible by the use of wrought iron. In suspension bridges, where the safety of the entire structure depended on the strength of each link, this called for much more careful quality control of the material than before. The thin plates and sections used in beams and trusses introduced for the first time the danger of failure by buckling. In general, the wider choice of structural types and the greater precision required in design added immensely to the skill and the intuitive sense of what was structurally sound which were demanded of the designer.

At the same time, however, he began to relinquish complete control of the design and construction process. The early Victorian engineers found it necessary to put the execution of some of their vast works in the hands of skilled employees who set up contracting firms and quoted for the job. This trend continued, and although there have been and still are many firms which offer both to design and construct, and a great deal of smaller structural work is carried out by authorities directly, with their own labour force, design and construction became, by and large, separate operations carried out by different people with, to some extent, different expertise. This division of labour, difficult though it would have been to avoid, has had an unfortunate effect on structural engineering: designs are produced too often without a clear understanding of how the structure is to be built, and the contractor, being unaware of the precise reasons for various design details may unwittingly fall into serious error. One important reason for the collapse of the first Quebec Bridge was lack of liaison between the contractors and the designer, the veteran engineer Theodore Cooper, who never once visited the site during construction. This was a rare and extreme example of what this dichotomy can lead to, but it is a fairly common complaint of contractors that the structures which they are invited to build have been designed without proper knowledge of or regard for the construction processes necessary to bring them into being. One consequence of this is that the structure may be unnecessarily expensive. It is becoming more and more common nowadays for contractors to be given the opportunity when tendering for a contract to submit their own alternative designs; but this is wasteful too, for only one of those submitted by different tenderers, if any at all, will be accepted. Two of the most brilliantly successful structural designers of today—Sir Ove Arup in England and Pier Luigi Nervi in Italy—have themselves built as well as designed their structures and have written convincingly on how desirable this procedure is.

Nowadays the variety of alternative materials and structural types which confront the designer of, for example, a highway bridge over a major river 300 m wide is bewildering. Here are some of the factors that will influence the design. It may be necessary to provide a certain minimum width of freeway and of clearance under the bridge for river traffic: the first will limit the freedom of the designer to choose the length of the spans, and the second may affect the general design and may well increase the length of the bridge. There may be no river traffic of importance, the river bed may be shallow and pier foundations cheap to construct: if so, and the height of the roadway above the bed is not great, there would be a case for a large number of short spans. The cost, per unit length of the bridge, of the superstructure on top of the piers, of whatever type it is (arches, beams, trusses, or whatever other structural type) increases with the span length, so that from the point of view of the cost of the superstructure, if only one structural type is being considered the shorter the spans the better. On the other hand, the more piers and foundations there are, the more expensive these become. As a very rough rule to start with, it used to be assumed that the cheapest design would be the one in which the costs, per unit length of the bridge, of the superstructure and of the piers and foundations were equal; but for accurate estimating a number of designs have to be run out and costed, and this is a task demanding great skill and experience.

The choice of superstructure affects these calculations profoundly, of course, and the most economical type of superstructure varies with the span. Excellent rock foundations at either side of the river and a roadway high above water level may make a single arch the most attractive solution, as at Gladesville. But in what material? Reinforced concrete or

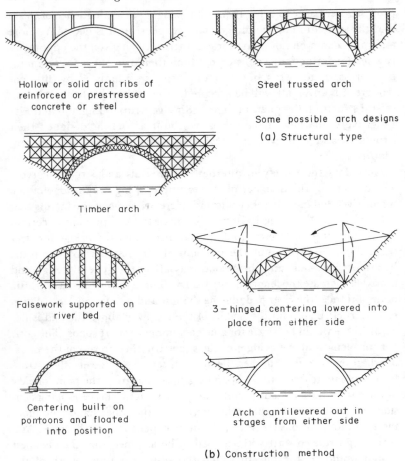

Hollow or solid arch ribs of
reinforced or prestressed
concrete or steel

Steel trussed arch

Some possible arch designs

(a) Structural type

Timber arch

Falsework supported on
river bed

3 – hinged centering lowered into
place from either side

Centering built on
pontoons and floated
into position

Arch cantilevered out in
stages from either side

(b) Construction method

FIG. 11.13. Some alternative solutions to the problem of designing and constructing an arched river bridge.

prestressed concrete and with solid ribs or hollow? Steel ribs or a steel truss, as in the Sydney Harbour bridge? Three-hinged, two-hinged, or fixed-ended? In inaccessible country with good materials and the necessary skills available locally, even a trussed timber arch may be feasible (Fig. 11.13a). Again, how is the arch to be built? By supporting it on false work, spanning across the river or resting on the river bed, by

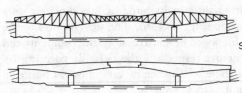

Steel cantilevered trusses

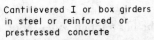

Cantilevered I or box girders
in steel or reinforced or
prestressed concrete

Continuous steel box girder

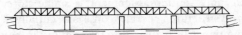

Multiple simply supported
spans (steel trusses, box or
I girders in steel, reinforced
or prestressed concrete)

Steel or reinforced concrete
bowstring girders

Cable either
tied to deck or
anchored to
abutment
at ends

Tied, anchored or prestressed
suspension bridge

Multiple concrete, brick or
stone arches

FIG. 11.14. Some other alternative designs for a river crossing.

cantilevering it out from either side, or by building it completely on a raft and floating it into position (Fig. 11.13b)? The site conditions, the material, perhaps the need for speed of construction, the problems and cost of maintaining the structure (especially the periodic painting required if steel is used) — all these and other factors must be borne in mind by the engineer in coming to a decision.

Where local conditions do not point clearly to the choice of an arch, he has a much wider set of alternatives, some (though not all) of which are shown in Fig. 11.14, and he must know how much each is likely to cost in the context of local availability of labour and materials.

The design of a river crossing such as this one is not, of course, a common occurrence in the average structural engineer's life. But to achieve an economical result the structural form must always be chosen carefully. For instance, in a much more routine assignment, a single storey steel factory building, the steel structure generally consists essentially of columns spaced on a rectangular grid, valley girders spanning in one direction over the columns, conventional roof trusses spanning in the other direction over the girders, and, resting on the truss rafters, purlins in angle or other section which support the roof covering (Fig. 11.15a). Firstly, it is a general principle of economical construction that the loads should be supported with a minimum of bending and carried to ground as quickly as possible. If the client wants wide clear open spaces he must realize that this will cost considerably more than if the columns are closely spaced, for, very roughly, the weight of the steelwork per unit area of floor increases in proportion to the span of the trusses. If he is wise, therefore, he will consider carefully how closely he can space the columns without interfering with the operations in the factory. Again, using two trusses per bay instead of three, as at (b), can increase the weight of trusses and purlins per unit of floor area by some 20 per cent, according to some figures given by L. R. Creasy, because although the trusses weigh slightly less the purlins are much heavier owing to their greater span. Further, the rectangular grid shown at (b) is more economical than a square grid having the same plan area and truss spacing (Fig. 11.15c) because the valley girders are more expensive in the latter.

Much greater economy is achieved by careful attention to the structural type to be adopted, and to the proportions of the structural frame,

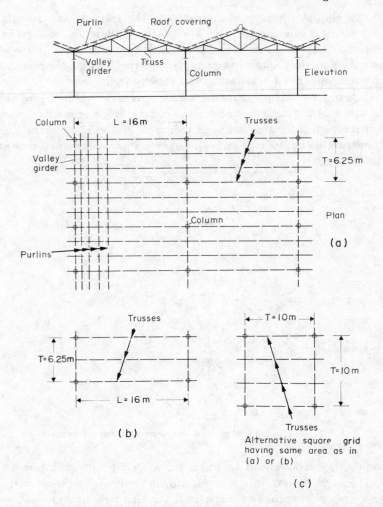

FIG. 11.15. Effect of plan layout on economics of single-storey factory construction in steel.

than by refinements in the structural design of the individual components — the purlins, trusses, etc., in the factory example — important though this of course is. Unfortunately, the teaching of structural engineering is still heavily biased towards the analysis and, to a less extent, the design of the structural parts, and time and experience are required before the young engineer appreciates the overriding importance of getting the initial broad structural concept right.

If there are so many alternative solutions to structural problems like the bridge and factory we have been discussing, is it ever possible to say that the perfect solution has been found? A bridge in the shape of a Pratt truss, let us say (Fig. 11.16a), can be designed for a single type of

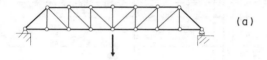

(a)

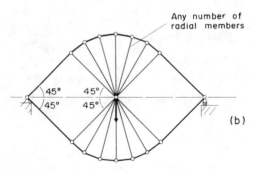

Any number of radial members

(b)

Fig. 11.16. Effect of configuration on economics of framed structures.

loading, say a downward central load, so that all the members are equally stressed, and since it is statically determinate the stress in the members will bear the same relation to the load right up to failure, so that at that point all the members will be at the limit of their strength in tension or compression. This may be considered perfectly efficient, but might not some other ratio of depth D to width W of bay give a lighter structure? Further, might not some other type of truss be lighter still? Some interesting theoretical work on this subject nearly a century ago in Australia showed, surprisingly, that the lightest structure for supporting a load at the middle of a span, though it was framed, bore no resemblance to any of the conventional types of truss (Fig. 11.16b). Unfortunately, little use can be made of this discovery because nearly all engineering structures have to support a variety of loads acting at various points and in different directions. For each load a different ideal configuration exists, but it is very doubtful whether one could ever be found to suit a variety of loading conditions. The experienced designer would object to the shape of the structure of Fig. 11.16b on purely practical grounds — its depth, for instance, could cause difficulties — and in any case the cheapest structure is not necessarily the lightest. Structural design involves many more factors than minimum weight, there are usually many reasonable alternative solutions, and there is seldom one which is clearly outstanding. In the end it is a matter of choice, of engineering judgement, perhaps of aesthetic preference.

Today the structural designer has many more tools at his disposal than ever before. Models were used as an aid to architectural design at least as early as the Renaissance: they occur in the notebooks of Leonardo da Vinci, and are known to have been made for important buildings like St. Peter's in Rome. As we saw in Chapter 3 (Fig. 3.28) Danisy in the eighteenth century used models to observe how arches collapse. But it seems certain that it was not until the nineteenth century that structural models were used in a quantitative sense to determine the behaviour of a structure under load. Telford, Brunel, and Robert Stephenson all built and tested large models of their major bridges. To aid in the design of the great box girders of the Britannia Bridge, small tubes of various cross-sectional shapes were first tested. These confirmed theoretical analyses which suggested that a rectangular cross-section would be best, and a model girder no less than 23 m long (a one-sixth scale model of the final girders) was then tested six times to failure, with repairs and modifications after each test until the weaknesses revealed by the failures had been rectified. By this process, combined with theoretical analyses, Stephenson and his advisers Fairbairn and Hodgkinson were confident not only of the ultimate strength of the girders but also of their behaviour, and especially their flexural stiffness, under service loads (it was essential to know this in order to carry out the prestressing process described in Chapter 8).

Structural models are used today mainly for unusual structures for which the available methods of structural analysis, whether for elastic design or to predict the ultimate strength, involve simplications and approximations the effects of which need to be verified. For elastic analysis the model need not be of the same material as that of the completed structure, so long as it behaves elastically: the model of the Academy of Science building in Canberra, for example (Fig. 9.13), was made of layers of fibre glass bonded with resin. Models intended for ultimate strength tests must, however, simulate the actual structure as closely as possible, both in material and in detailed form, and be as large as is feasible, otherwise some potentially dangerous detail may not be reproduced.

The first high-speed electronic digital computer, to give it its full title, was built in the U.S.A. immediately after the end of the Second World War. It included thousands of conventional thermionic valves and would have filled an ordinary house. Since then computers have become much more compact, much faster and more powerful, and far easier to use, and today the engineer can solve in a matter of minutes a structural problem which would take him months by the hand methods of calculation, or which he might never be able to solve because of its complexity.

Furthermore (and this has happened only in the last 10 years or so) it is now possible not only to find the forces, stresses, and deflections set up in a given structure: the computer can be instructed to check the adequacy of the structure and, if necessary, modify the proportions of the members to meet the required standards of strength and stiffness. It can produce detailed cross-sections, reinforcement, and even working drawings. Of course, computers will only do what they are told, and the designer will always retain control of the critical decisions. But the facility and cheapness with which alternative designs can now be produced are of inestimable value in arriving at the "best" solution.

These developments have been so rapid that they have taken engineering educators by surprise, but they raise issues of basic importance. The first effect of the computer revolution on structural engineering was that it forced designers to re-examine their methods of analysis. These were a miscellaneous assortment of apparently unrelated methods, some of which had been ingeniously devised to avoid the need to solve large numbers of linear simultaneous equations by the usual methods. It was soon found necessary to systematize the approach to analysis so that problems could be presented to the computer in the logical, orderly way it appreciates, and indeed requires.

But an even more basic question is this: to analyse a structure far more complicated than he could ever tackle by the old hand methods, the engineer now has only to feed into the computer the basic information about the structure and the loads, and a standard programme which was written by a specialist will produce the answer for him. Is it still necessary in structural engineering courses, therefore, to spend a great deal of time on methods of *analysis* of structures, as has been the case in the past? There is clearly an opportunity now to place greater emphasis on the physical behaviour of structures and on how they are *designed* rather than merely analysed.

Structural design is an art as well as a science. Outstanding modern structural engineers like Arup, Torroja, Nervi, and Leonhardt have all had, firstly, a profound understanding of structural behaviour, of how, structures of different types and in different materials transmit force and how they respond in stress and deflection. They conceive their designs in broad terms, thinking first of the appropriate structural form, and checking its validity and dimensions with simple calculations. Cost is never far from their minds. Sophisticated structural analyses, where they are necessary, are a secondary step. In the elaboration of the initial concept, attention to detail is extremely important because, as we will see in the next chapter, minor, often insignificant defects are a major cause of structural failures. The best structural designers are also artists because, like potters, they take a material and shape it, almost intuitively, into a useful and attractive form. Like the potter, the apparent ease with which strikingly different designs are produced is based on a down-to-earth technical mastery of the medium. How these processes can be conveyed to students is the principal challenge before teachers of structural engineering today.

CHAPTER 12

Some Structural Failures and Their Lessons

BEFORE THE nineteenth century, when methods of structural analysis became available which enabled the strength of a projected structure to be estimated with at least some degree of certainty, the designer faced with the task of producing a structure much bigger or different in type from what had been done successfully before had little choice but to proceed on the basis of trial and error. Not surprisingly, in periods of rapid structural experimentation and development there were many failures either during construction or in service. This was particularly the case during the Roman Empire and the Gothic period of cathedral building in western Europe in the Middle Ages.

The cathedral of Aya Sofya (the Divine Wisdom) in Istanbul was completed in A.D. 537 to the orders of the Emperor Justinian. The central dome A (Fig. 12.1) has a diameter of 32.5 m, a considerable span for those days. It is not supported directly off the ground by walls or col-

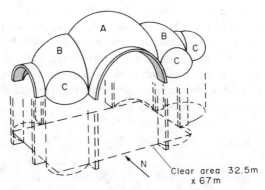

FIG. 12.1. Structural scheme of Cathedral of Aya Sofya, Istanbul.

260

umns, however, but by arches on all four sides, and on the east and west sides, in addition, by secondary half-domes B as well as still smaller domes C, so as to provide a clear interior space unimpeded by columns of no less than 32.5 m by 67 m, much greater than in any previous building. Without any reliable quantitative structural theory to guide them, but evidently with an intuitive understanding of how loads are transmitted through a complex assembly of brick domes and arches, the architects succeeded in erecting one of the most interesting and audacious structures of all time.

The present form was not arrived at, however, without many mishaps and subsequent modifications. These are described in detail in Mainstone's splendidly definitive work, *Developments in Structural Form*; but, briefly, even while it was still under construction, spreading of the east and west arches called for substantial additions to the buttressed supports. Then in A.D. 558 the eastern part of the cupola collapsed while repairs were underway after one of the periodic earthquakes which led to, but were not the sole cause of, the strengthening which was done at various times at least up to the fourteenth century.

The Gothic cathedral builders were even more adventurous, and their delicate stone skeletons with their ribbed vaults, slender columns, and flying buttresses within which tremendous static forces are poised in equilibrium, still amaze the structural engineer. The final form of Gothic construction was achieved in the main through successive experiments and failures extending over much of the twelfth and thirteenth centuries. As the height and span of the nave vault were increased and columns became more and more slender, the outward thrust of the roof reached a point where outside propping was essential to prevent collapse when the supports under the vault were removed. The first flying buttresses, according to Mainstone, were actually applied as hasty expedients to prevent a threatened vault collapse, or in reconstructions after a collapse had occurred. The slenderness of Gothic construction reached its limit in Beauvais Cathedral, the vaults of which collapsed in 1284, 12 years after they had been finished. In no later Gothic building were its proportions repeated.

In making use of structural failures to extend the limits of practicability of a form of construction, the Gothic master builders were aided by the fact that their structures were very heavy in comparison with the wind loads likely to come on them. Once they had been successfully erected free of the construction supports, they were unlikely to collapse later unless the margin of safety against failure was so narrow that creep in the mortar joints between the stones, or settlement of the foundations, was sufficient to create a collapse mechanism in the stone skeleton.

Foundations, as Pugsley has remarked, were the Achilles heel of mediaeval construction—many of the Gothic cathedrals were built on very soft, waterlogged ground, and downward settlement and outward spread of the principal foundations under the nave and tower not infrequently caused such distortion of the fabric that, even where actual collapse did not occur, extensive strengthening was necessary, as at Wells, for example.

The next great leap forward in the form and size of structures occurred in the nineteenth century, and it is a tribute to the genius of the great structural engineers of that time that until the last quarter of the century there were very few major structural failures except in railway bridges of cast iron, which could not stand the impact loading of trains, and in suspension bridges, which have special problems to which we will refer later. Then, in December 1879, Britain was shocked by the collapse in a gale of the main spans of the railway bridge across the Firth of Tay which had been officially opened only 18 months before. A train was crossing the bridge at the time, and all 75 people in it died. The bridge was by no means revolutionary in form or size: it consisted of 98 lattice girder spans, only the central 13 of which were of substantial size (11 of 75-m span and 2 of 69 m). These spans were supported on piers, each consisting of six hollow cast iron columns 0.38 m and 0.46 m in diameter, braced together (Fig. 7.8). Apparently the river foundations, as a rule the main difficulty in such a bridge, were constructed without incident. But, as was noted in Chapter 11, no allowance had been made for wind pressure in the design; and the quality of the materials, especially the cast iron used in the piers, was atrocious, the contractor was allowed to get away with appalling workmanship (bolts and rivets were missing and vital tie members were slack), and the bridge was not properly maintained while in service. It is possible, as was suggested in Chapter 7, that torsional instability of the piers may have been a contributory factor in the failure. It was a terrible lesson in the need for good standards of design, construction, and maintenance: so terrible that the designer, Sir Thomas Bouch, died of a broken heart less than a year later.

In August 1907, the Quebec railway bridge across the St. Lawrence River in Canada collapsed while it was still under construction, with the death of 74 men. It would have been the world's largest steel bridge of the cantilever type (Fig. 12.2), with a central span of 549 m, 27 m

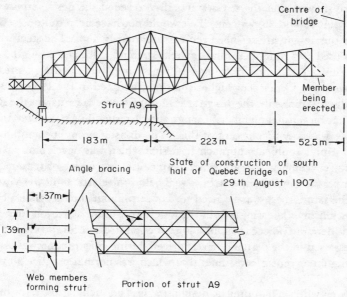

FIG. 12.2. Failure of first Quebec Bridge.

longer than those of the Forth railway bridge, completed 17 years earlier. Its designer, Theodore Cooper, a distinguished bridge engineer at the end of a long and successful career, undertook the task for a fee of $22,500, less than 1 per cent of the cost of the bridge, and was consequently unable to engage enough trained and experienced staff to assist him. Cooper was unwell, never once visited the site during construction and only paid three visits to the fabrication shops where the steelwork was being assembled. Lack of adequate support staff meant that the designs could not be exhaustively checked, or the construction properly supervised.

In February 1906, when the design, including the detailing of the members and connections, was complete and much of the steelwork had actually been fabricated, it was found (as was noted in Chapter 11) that the dead weight of the bridge had been underestimated by no less than 24 per cent. Cooper calculated that this would cause a 7 to 10 per cent increase in maximum stresses, though investigations made after the collapse showed that the stresses actually exceeded the design stresses by between 10 and 25 per cent. This would not have been quite so serious had the design stresses not been extraordinarily high. The steel which was used was roughly similar in yield strength, ultimate strength, and ductility to that used in bridges 50 years later, but the design stress in tension was 19 per cent higher than that adopted in the 1950s in steel bridges. Worse still, the design stress for fairly stocky struts was the same as that for tension members, though the corresponding stress used in the 1950s was only 67 per cent of this. (The disaster brought to an abrupt end a philosophical approach to design which was developing at that time, in which it was argued that since the behaviour of tension and compression members at stresses well below the elastic limit was virtually the same, there was no need for concern about the fact that a compression member would fail at a lower stress than a tension member, and therefore no occasion for a lower design stress in compression.) The stress used in the design of rivets driven during construction was no less than 46 per cent greater than that which was normal practice 50 years later.

Even with such optimistic design stresses and such a gross error in the calculation of the dead weight of the bridge, it would probably not have collapsed had the main compression members been properly designed. The two struts which failed (A9, Fig. 12.2) and precipitated the collapse consisted of four web members laced together by the lightest of steel angle bars with only one rivet at each end. They had been designed on the basis of small-scale tests 20 years earlier on struts with only one-thirtieth the cross sectional area of struts A9. In the design it was assumed that the lacing bars would constrain the webs to bend as a fairly stocky unit when the strut came under compression and the inevitable eccentricity of loading and deviations from perfect straightness caused it to bend sideways. In fact, they were not strong enough for this, and the webs tended to act as four independent, much slenderer and therefore much weaker struts. One-third scale model struts (which would be big enough to reproduce reasonably well the details in the full-scale members) tested after the disaster failed at an average axial stress only 79 per cent of the design stress used for these members. The stress in struts A9 at the moment of failure, calculated afterwards, was within six per cent of this. Ironically, the tests also showed that when the lacing bars were made 50 per cent heavier and attached to the web members with two rivets at each end instead of one, the axial stress at failure of the model struts rose to 12 per cent *above* the design stress—a 40 per cent increase in strength could thus have been achieved at very little cost.

The bridge was undoubtedly doomed before it left the drawing-board. Nevertheless, the structure gave ample warning of the impending disaster. Weeks before it fell, bowing of the struts and bulging of the splice plates at their ends had been noticed. One week before, the bowing in one strut was 20 mm; five days later it had increased to 57 mm. Rivets began to shear off, the structure was creaking and obviously on the move, the workmen were apprehensive. On the morning of 29 August, Cooper was consulted in New York and sent a cable (which was not delivered to the site) ordering work to be halted "until after due consideration of facts". The bridge collapsed at 3.30 p.m.

After the Tay disaster, wind pressure was properly allowed for; after Quebec, great attention was devoted to the design of built-up struts; and both failures underlined the need for better control over the quality of the materials used, and for high standards of construction. The defects in design, construction, or organization which a major structural failure reveals are, in fact, usually taken so very much to heart by the engineering profession that they are avoided in later work. This was not so in the case of suspension bridges. The earliest cable or chain bridges were notorious for their flexibility and their tendency to build up large oscillations in the wind or under repeated impulses from the steps of marching men. A bridge built by James Finley, one of the pioneers of suspension bridges in the U.S.A., collapsed in 1809 under a drove of cattle. One with a span of 132 m designed by Sir Samuel Brown, another pioneer, at Montrose in Scotland fell into the River Esk when a crowd of people watching a boat race rushed from one side to the other. Another by the same engineer, the chain pier at Brighton, which had four spans each of 78 m, was partially destroyed in a gale in 1833, eleven years after it was opened. Telford's Menai bridge was damaged by gales even during construction, and was lucky not to be destroyed in the years that followed (vertical oscillations up to 5 m were observed during storms) before the deck was stiffened by the addition of trusses. In 1849 the River Ohio was spanned at Wheeling, W. Virginia, by the first suspension bridge with a main span of more than 1000 ft. The deck was only 6 m wide and its only stiffening was the parapets. It very soon collapsed during a cool breeze, according to an eye-witness account quoted by Hopkins, which describes the structure as "heaving and dashing with tremendous force . . . lunging like a ship in a storm . . . (it) rose nearly to the height of the tower, then fell, and twisted and writhed . . . At last there seemed to be a determined twist along the entire span, about one-half of the flooring being nearly reversed, and down went the structure . . . with an appalling crash and roar."

One would have thought that such a disaster would never be allowed to occur again, especially as it was by no means an isolated event. Yet this description exactly fits what happened to the Tacoma Narrows bridge across Puget Sound, Washington, U.S.A. in November 1940, only four months after it had been opened to traffic, and after an hour in a wind of only 68 km/hr. As we noted in Chapter 9, a cable bridge with a deck which has little longitudinal stiffness is extremely flexible even under loads which are virtually static: one of Brown's bridges, over the River Tees in Durham, was nearly destroyed when a locomotive train ventured on it. But a different kind of hazard arises in wind, as the model experiments conducted after the Tacoma disaster demonstrated. The deck of this bridge, which with a main span of 854 m was the third largest then constructed, was stiffened by plate girders (Fig. 12.3). Smoke stream studies on a model of the bridge showed that vortices would develop above and below the deck at intervals depending on the wind speed. The pressure differences set up by the vortices tended to amplify the vertical movement, especially if they were created at intervals which tied in with the period of vertical oscillation of the bridge itself. If the bridge deck had poor torsional stiffness, it would tend to twist, and this would greatly increase the upward and downward forces.

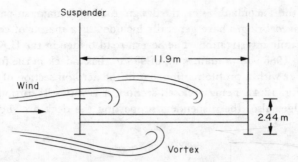

FIG. 12.3. Cross-section of deck of Tacoma Narrows Bridge, Washington, U.S.A.

The actual wind speed was shown to be quite critical: if it was too high the vortices moved off the bridge more quickly and had less effect, while if it was too low a vortex would remain on the deck after the upward movement had begun. In the bridge itself, at a wind of 62 km/hr the vertical movements were moderate (about a metre) with the two suspension cables in phase. But when the wind speed changed to 68 km/hr the period of oscillation suddenly increased threefold and the vertical movements leaped up to nearly 10 m. Worse still, the oscillations of the two suspension cables were now out of phase, one going up while the other went down, with torsional movements which sent the deck into a sideways slope of 45°. No structure could stand such gross distortion for long, especially since the deck, being an open section, had a very low torsional strength, and the stiffening girders broke off and the deck fell into the river, fortunately without loss of life.

Ironically, the phenomenon was one which was similar in principle to that of "flutter" of the wings of aircraft, and aeronautical engineers had already learned to avoid the danger that wings might break off in flight through aerodynamic instability. In aeronautical terms, the Tacoma deck section had negative lift characteristics. But bridge engineers were apparently unaware of the work which had been done in this closely related field. Suspension bridges were built on more and more slender lines in spite of many danger signals (for example, the Golden Gate bridge, completed in 1937, oscillated vertically as much as 5 m before the deck was strengthened at a cost of $3m) and in ignorance of existing aeroelastic theory.

Since the Tacoma disaster, the design studies for major suspension or cable-stayed bridges have generally included as a matter of course an aerodynamic investigation. The Severn road bridge in the U.K., completed in 1966 with a main span of 988 m, has a deck in the form of a box girder with a profile reminiscent of the aerofoil section of aircraft wings (Fig. 12.4). Being a closed section, it is very stiff torsionally. In this bridge, also, the suspenders supporting the deck are slightly in-

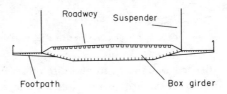

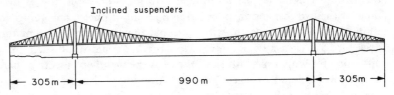

FIG. 12.4. Cross-section of deck and general elevation of Severn Bridge, U.K.

clined to give a certain degree of triangulation, which provides some measure of rigidity in the structure considered as a framework. But perhaps the suspension bridge of the future will be the pre-stressed cable truss which was described in Chapter 8 (see Fig. 8.14). Aerodynamic stability is ensured by the triangulated system of members which are all maintained in tension by the prestressing forces even under the worst conditions of loading. Some very large bridges of this type have been built: the Volgograd bridge over the River Volga, for example, has a main span of 874 m.

The Quebec bridge actually failed twice. When it was redesigned it was decided to build the 5200 tonne suspended span elsewhere, float it into position and jack it up onto its bearings. When it had been raised 4 m a casting fractured and the span crashed into the river, killing another 11 men. This was a material failure; cast iron is by nature brittle. But, as was pointed out in Chapter 6, normally ductile steel can also fail in a brittle manner under certain circumstances. Welded steel structures are particularly prone to brittle fracture unless care is taken.

In March 1938 the Hasselt bridge over the Albert Canal in Belgium suddenly collapsed just after a cyclist had crossed it. Soon afterwards another similar bridge over the canal also failed. Both were welded steel Vierendeel (open web) girders with curved upper chords, and they simply broke up into a number of pieces just as if they had been made of unreinforced concrete. During the Second World War a number of the welded Liberty cargo ships which were mass-produced in American shipyards broke up at sea; one, the *Schenectady*, actually broke in half while it was lying quietly at its moorings being fitted out after launching. In all, over 400 cases of fracture of welded ships were recorded. Not long after the war, the Duplessis bridge in Canada, a multi-span continuous steel girder bridge, collapsed in very cold weather, and there were other welded bridges in which the steel behaved in an alarming way, as though it had no ductility. One of these was King's Bridge, in Melbourne, Australia.

King's Bridge, as was noted briefly in Chapter 8, consists of a large number of simply supported plate girder spans carrying a highway across the River Yarra in the centre of the city. On a cold but not freezing morning in July 1962, fifteen months after it had been opened to traffic, the four girders in one of the end spans fractured after the passage of a low loader and trailer well under the permissible weight. Complete collapse of the span was prevented by lateral retaining walls, no one was injured, and the failure was ignominious rather than spectacular. The girders were of a medium high-strength steel with a yield strength some 35 per cent higher than that of mild steel and with somewhat lower but still good ductility (18 per cent extension on a 200-mm gauge-length). They were built up by welding two flange plates to a web plate. Additional flange metal was provided in the central part of the spans by welding cover plates on to the flange plates as shown in

Fig. 12.5. The cracks which led to the failure of the girders all started at the ends of the cover plates, and some had been there before the girders were painted — that is, while they were still in the fabricating shop. The cracks had progressed through the flange plate and up the web in several stages during the brief life of the structure, until so much of the web was cracked that the passage of the low loader completed the process of failure. The fractured surfaces were crystalline in appearance, like that of cast iron, rather than fibrous, as in ductile steel. Careful examination of the whole bridge revealed that there were similar cracks in many other places. Had the failure occurred elsewhere, at a point where the bridge crossed over a busy road, it might have caused considerable loss of life.

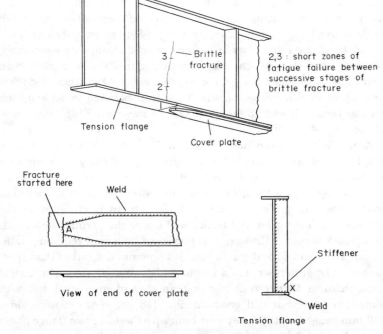

FIG. 12.5. Details of welded plate girder of King's Bridge, Melbourne, Australia.

As a result of this and other failures from brittle fracture, and the investigations prompted by them, the phenomenon is now well understood and can be guarded against. Solid materials, as we saw in Chapter 2, have a brittle (or tensile) strength and a yield (or shear) strength. The brittle strength is not very sensitive to temperature, but the yield strength increases sharply as the material gets colder. Whether it be steel or sealing wax, therefore, the likelihood that a material will fracture rather than deform plastically under a given state of stress increases as the ambient temperature falls.

Another important factor is stress. As was noted in Chapter 6, if there is a state of tensile triaxial stress in the material, failure is very likely to be by fracture rather than by plastic flow, even if the material is ductile under more normal (uniaxial) tensile stress conditions. Triaxial tensile stresses, as we saw, are set up around discontinuities such as holes, cracks, and changes in cross-section when a member is subjected to tension or even, in some circumstances, to compression. Furthermore, when a steel member is welded, *residual* tensile stresses are left after the welding is completed. These vary in magnitude with the details of the parts being welded together, and in particular with the degree of restraint against freedom of movement of the parts. For example, if a short piece of steel is welded at its ends to a heavy, virtually rigid block of steel (Fig. 12.6) very high tensile stresses will be set up as the piece cools and shrinks after welding. In King's Bridge, the ends A of the cover plates (Fig. 12.5) were welded last, after the rest of the welding had been completed, and the weld at A was not able to shrink freely, so that high residual tensile stresses were created which were triaxial because of the shape of the detail.

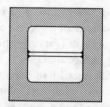

FIG. 12.6. Bar welded at ends to rigid supports.

Another factor is rate of application of stress. As we saw in Chapter 2, the more rapidly a piece of material is loaded, the more likely it is to fail by fracture rather than by plastic flow. For this reason, standard tests for brittleness of steels are always carried out with suddenly applied loads.

In King's Bridge further difficulties were caused by the nature of the steel. Its high strength derived from the addition of manganese and chromium, and from a somewhat higher percentage of carbon than in mild steel. Unfortunately, these elements also increase the tendency of the steel to "notch brittleness" (that is, to a brittle form of failure in a specimen with a notch in it, when subjected to a sudden tensile force). They also increase the likelihood that the metal adjacent to the welds, which is heated during the welding process, will become hard and brittle on cooling and perhaps develop cracks. It was not fully realized that extra precautions—in particular, preheating the metal around the region to be welded so that it did not cool too quickly after welding, the best sequence of welding so as to minimize residual stresses, the use of special welding electrodes, and keeping the work dry so as to avoid the danger of embrittlement caused by hydrogen penetrating into the welded metal—were necessary with this steel compared with normal welding practice in mild steel. Some of the steel, also, was found to be more notch-brittle than was permitted by the specification.

As a result of all these factors, the steel in the heat-affected zones adjacent to the welds at the ends of the cover plates was embrittled by the welding process, and was extensively cracked during fabrication. The steel outside these zones was more notch-brittle than ordinary mild steel. There were high residual tensile stresses around these welds. When the bridge was loaded, further tensile stresses, also triaxial at these points because of the discontinuity in cross-section, were set up. The shock caused by the passage of a vehicle on a cold morning was sufficient to start the final process of fracture which broke the span; but its fate had been sealed long before that.

Ironically, the cover plate detail had been more or less forced on the designers because it was known that thick plates tend to be more notch-brittle than thin ones. To *avoid* the danger of brittle fracture, therefore, a limit of 25 mm was set on the thickness of the flange plates. Because there were also restrictions on the *width* of the flange plates to safeguard against local buckling (see Fig. 7.5f), this obliged the designers to provide the extra flange cross-sectional area required near midspan by adding cover plates, and so, unwittingly, to design the detail at which failure occurred. It would have been better to use a thicker flange plate in the central section of the girders and join it to the thinner plate by butt-welds (which are relatively free from residual stress) with a gently tapered length to avoid a stress raiser at the change in section (Fig. 12.7). Nowadays the need for thick plates can be avoided altogether by

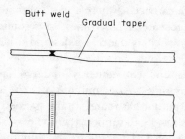

FIG. 12.7. Butt-welded flange plate joint as alternative to adding a cover plate where greater thickness is needed.

using box-section girders, in which a much greater width of flange is possible than in the conventional plate girder. Nevertheless, the detail would probably have been adequate if the steel had been of better quality and proper welding procedures had been followed.

Brittle fractures require an initiator—a minute crack in or near a weld, a sharp discontinuity in the shape of the member, a roughly drilled hole, or even an arc "strike" (caused when the welder scratches his electrode on the surface of the steel to bare the metal core, and it arcs momentarily) is enough. Once it starts, a fracture continues at great speed, since the stress needed to propagate the fracture is less than that required to start it. It stops when there is no longer enough energy available to continue to create the two new surfaces of metal along the fracture. In a statically determinate situation, as when a simply supported girder fractures at the tension flange, it will break right through unless the steel is much less notch-brittle further up the web. In statically indeterminate situations, the fracture may well stop as stress is redistributed to adjoining regions of the structure. In all cases, however, brittle fracture is an extremely dangerous phenomenon. It can be safeguarded against firstly by making sure that the steel is notch-ductile, and then by good design of details, appropriate welding techniques, and rigorous inspection procedures during construction and afterwards in service.

Close inspection of the fractured girders of King's Bridge showed that the successive stages of brittle fracture in the web were separated by very short lengths with a quite different appearance, smooth, striated, and "soapy" to the touch. This is characteristic of failure by fatigue, a phenomenon which can occur where a piece of material is subjected to stresses which are repeated many times. It is common in the moving parts of machinery, such as the rear axles and driving shafts of motor vehicles, in locomotive rails, and in parts of bridges which directly support moving loads and consequently undergo large stress changes repeated very many times. After millions of steps have been taken, it even occurs, as the author has found, in the stainless steel pads worn by some people in their shoes to support the arches of the feet. Because of the high incidence of fatigue failure in aluminium alloy aircraft, especially during and after the Second World War, the phenomenon has been most intensively studied in the aircraft industry. In the King's Bridge girders, brittle fracture proceeded to a point where the remaining strain energy in the surrounding material could no longer maintain the process. From then on, repetitions of live load stress caused a very gradual extension of the crack as a fatigue failure, until a combination of circumstances — stress, shock, low temperature and perhaps a change in the properties of the steel in the web — set off the fracture process again.

When a metal structure is subjected to a large number of cycles of loading, a fatigue crack can start at a stress raiser — a sudden change in the cross-section, a rivet hole, a weld crack. Once started, it is its own stress raiser and progresses very gradually until the structure is so weakened that it fails. Cracking can develop even though the ambient stress, not taking account of local stress concentrations, is below the elastic limit of the material. The most spectacular structural fatigue failures were probably those of three Comet airliners in the early 1950s. The cabins were pressurized during each flight, and the holes left in the fuselage by the cabin windows created a stress raiser. A further stress raiser was caused by the fairly sharp corners of the windows and the riveting around them. Usually millions of repetitions of stress are required to produce a fatigue failure; in the Comets it occurred after only a few thousand cycles of pressurizing, which was completely unexpected, but full-scale tests on the Comet fuselage fully confirmed the cause of the accidents. Fatigue cannot be avoided in aircraft, but it can be anticipated (although to predict the *precise* number of flying hours at which a plane will fail, as in Nevil Shute's dramatization of aircraft fatigue, *No Highway*, is still far from possible) and periodic inspection and repair at known trouble spots is now normal procedure. Full-scale prototypes of each new model of aircraft are, of course, subjected to extensive fatigue testing during the design process, and its fatigue characteristics are well understood.

Civil engineering structures like bridges are not tested in this rigorous way—the cost would be prohibitive in "one-off" designs—but enough is now known about various kinds of detail to guide the designer. The design stress depends on the number of repetitions of stress to be expected during the life of the structure. It is much less for a detail like the King's Bridge cover plates than for the alternative butt-welded joint of Fig. 12.7, especially if the welds are dressed level with the surface of the plates. Generally, detailing which safeguards the structure from brittle fracture is also good against fatigue. Insignificant details can substantially reduce the fatigue strength: for example, it is bad practice to weld web stiffeners to the tension flange, as at point X in Fig. 12.5, because this disturbs the smooth flow of stress along the flange and creates a sharp stress raiser. With steel one unfortunate fact is that its fatigue strength varies very little with its static strength, so that where fatigue considerations determine the design stresses there is very little advantage in using the higher strength steels. The greatest danger always arises where the stresses are completely reversed from tension to compression during each cycle, as in, for example, a steel chimney which oscillates in the wind (Fig. 11.2). Much of the damage caused to houses by the cyclone at Darwin, Australia, in 1974 arose from fatigue failure in steel roof sheeting around screw fastenings after the roof had vibrated violently for several hours at a few cycles a second. Once the roof had gone the house very soon collapsed. (Ironically, most of the roofs were adequately designed for *static* forces of the magnitudes experienced.) In bridges the most vulnerable parts are members like cross-girders, which directly support the traffic and undergo large cyclical variations of stress. The main members, especially in very large bridges where the dead load stresses are much greater than those due to live loads, are rarely a problem.

The first chapter of this book opened with a reference to another Melbourne disaster, the collapse in October 1970 of a 112-m span of the Westgate Bridge, then under construction. Westgate was basically a problem of flexural instability. As was pointed out in Chapter 7, buckling in one of its many forms has been a leading cause of structural failure, especially during construction, either in the structure itself or in the temporary supports (see Fig. 7.12, for example). Failure of the structural material, from brittle fracture, fatigue, or even from a change in the chemical constitution and a consequent loss of strength (as in the failure of high alumina cement concrete buildings in the U.K. and elsewhere, mentioned in Chapter 11) has also been fairly common. In most cases, the calculation of the forces in the various parts of the structure — what is generally understood as the structural analysis — has not been at fault, or at least not seriously so. But failure to design the details of the structure so that they will carry these forces satisfactorily is only too common, and has brought down more than one great bridge, as we have seen. The strength of a large structure can depend on small and apparently insignificant details — the welds at the ends of the cover plates in King's Bridge, for example, or the corners of the cabin windows in the Comet airliners. Structural analysis rarely reveals their importance, and it is highly desirable when a structure is contemplated which has new, untried features or is different in scale from what has been done before, to test models of the proposed structure, full-scale if necessary and possible, but at least large enough to reproduce the details reasonably well, as a part of the design process.

The partial collapse of the Ronan Point flats (Chapter 10) highlighted at least two other aspects of the design process. Firstly, the designer must visualize *all* the forces that his structure may have to resist, not simply those referred to in his structural code. Gas explosions are easily the most common unforeseen hazard which buildings may suffer from, as a survey in the U.K. in 1973 revealed, and it is obvious, in hindsight, that they should have been allowed for in the design of

Ronan Point and similar buildings. Secondly, the Ronan Point incident underlined the importance of ensuring that if one part of a structure fails unexpectedly, it should be capable of resisting progressive collapse like a house of cards by possessing a degree of continuity which will enable the forces in the structure to bridge the gap and take another path. This "fail-safe" philosophy was first developed for aircraft, but it is a sound approach to all structural design, and all structures should be examined during the design stage from this point of view. If the Empire State Building had been designed on the same principles as Ronan Point, the loss of life when it was struck by the bomber in 1945 would have been cataclysmic.

A contributory factor in many structural failures has been lack of effective communication between the parties concerned in the design, construction, and maintenance of the structure—this was the case in most of the examples cited in this chapter. It is essential that the intentions of the designer, the principles behind the design and the reasons for various details are well understood by those responsible for the construction, and, vice versa, that the designer is fully aware of the construction procedures which are proposed.

Structural engineers are continually facing new challenges which call for extrapolations of existing practice. For this reason alone, there will inevitably be failures from time to time. Oil-production platforms in steel were singled out as likely future candidates in an article in *New Scientist* in February 1976. The rules for safeguarding against buckling of the steel cylinders used in these huge structures, it was pointed out, are based on tests on rocket bodies made of aluminium alloy with stiffening fins riveted or machined on. The platform cylinders, however, are larger, and are welded, using high yield steel. No full-scale testing has been done. The loading conditions are not accurately known, but are extremely severe. To judge from past experience, some at least of the conditions for structural collapse are present here. Only time will tell whether the gloomy predictions of the *New Scientist* authors will be realized.

Glossary

ACTION. The main set of forces acting on a structure or structural element; also the manner in which forces are transmitted by a structure or structural element (as: direct action, bending action).

AISLE. The part of a longitudinally planned church or cathedral which flanks the nave.

AMPLITUDE. Relating to movement, the maximum value of the displacement to either side of a mean position during a periodic oscillation.

ANALYSIS. The determination of the state of a given structure, as regards stress, deflection, stability, or other condition, under specified loads. See also ELASTIC ANALYSIS, COLLAPSE ANALYSIS, LIMIT STATES ANALYSIS.

ANTICLASTIC. Referring to a surface having curvatures in opposite senses (concave and convex) in different directions at any point (as in a saddle-shaped roof).

ARCH. A structural element spanning a gap and capable of supporting loads mainly by compressive action.

BARREL VAULT. A vault having the profile of a curved arch and with the same cross-section throughout its length.

BEAM. A structural element which supports a load across a gap by bending action.

BENDING. A type of stressing of a structural element in which the stress varies across any cross section from a tensile maximum at one edge to a compressive maximum at the opposite edge, and in which an initially straight element becomes curved.

BENDING MOMENT. At a point in a beam in equilibrium, the sum of the moments of the forces acting on the beam to one side of the point; this must be opposed by the moment of resistance of the beam.

BOX GIRDER. A girder in the form of a hollow rectangular or other closed cross-section.

BRITTLE. Relating to a material, one which breaks with little prior plastic deformation.

BUCKLING. Failure of a structural element by compressive forces which cause it to bend laterally and suffer a rapid loss of stiffness.

BUTTRESS. A vertical or inclined structural element intended to resist outward thrusts in a building.

CABLE. A thin, long, flexible structural element capable of resisting direct tensile forces but having virtually no compressive or bending strength.

CAMBER. A slight upward curvature given to a beam or truss.

CANTILEVER. A beam or framework projecting outwards from a support.

CATENARY. The curve assumed by a continuous cable hanging under its own weight.

CENTERING. Temporary supports used to construct an arch or vault.

CHORD. One of the outer members in a truss.

COFFERDAM. A temporary wall of earth, timber, steel or concrete built around an area to keep water out during construction.

COLLAPSE ANALYSIS. One of the techniques available for calculating the loads necessary to cause a structure to collapse as a mechanism.

278

COUPLE.   A system of two equal but oppositely directed forces which tend to cause rotation.

CREEP.   Deformation occurring gradually over a period of time without increase in the load.

CRITICAL LOAD.   Relating to a strut or other compression member, the maximum load which the member can carry without buckling.

CROWN.   The highest point of an arch or vault.

DEAD LOAD.   The weight of a structure, as distinct from the live load carried by it.

DIAPHRAGM.   A thin transverse plate used to stiffen a thin-walled structure such as a shell or box girder.

DIRECT.   A type of stressing of a structural element in which the stress is uniform (either tensile or compressive) over any cross section, and the element shortens or extends but does not develop curvature.

DOME.   A shell, commonly in the form of a portion of a sphere, covering a circular area.

DUCTILE.   Relating to a material, one which is capable of carrying stress at or near the ultimate strength over a wide range of deformation.

ELASTIC ANALYSIS.   Determination of the forces, stresses, and deformations in a structure under a specified set of loads on the assumption that the material behaves elastically at all points.

ELASTIC DEFORMATION.   Deformation which disappears when the load is removed.

EQUILIBRIUM.   A state of a structure in which all the forces on it are in balance. If no dynamic forces are involved the equilibrium will be *static*, and the structure will be at rest.

EXTRADOS.   The upper or outside surface of an arch.

FACTOR OF SAFETY.   See STRESS FACTOR OF SAFETY; LOAD FACTOR OF SAFETY.

FALSEWORK.   Temporary supports during construction, especially of arches.

FATIGUE.   Failure by very slow development of cracks under a large number of repeated applications of load which individually would not cause distress.

FLANGE.   One of the portions of a beam or column of I, box or other section which help to resist bending action by almost pure tensile or compressive stress.

FLEXURAL INSTABILITY.   See BUCKLING.

FLYING BUTTRESS.   An inclined strut, normally of arched form, transmitting outward thrusts from a vault to an outer pier.

FORMWORK.   Temporary moulds in which concrete is placed, to give it a required shape.

FUNICULAR.   The shape assumed by a cable or system of cables.

GIRDER.   A term almost synonymous with beam, but used for larger sizes of beam, especially those built up from smaller sections.

GOLDEN SECTION.   Relating to a rectangle in which the ratio of the length of the shorter side to the longer is the same as the ratio of the difference between the lengths of the longer and shorter sides to the length of the shorter. This ratio is approximately 0.62.

GROINED VAULT.   A vault formed by the intersection of two barrel vaults.

GROUT.   A fluid mixture of neat cement and water or cement, sand, and water used to fill joints or other voids.

HINGE.   See PINNED JOINT.

HYPERBOLIC PARABOLOID.   A saddle-shaped surface generated by moving one straight line along two others placed skew to each other.

INSTABILITY.   A tendency to collapse.

INTRADOS.   The inner surface of an arch.

ISOTROPIC.   Of a material, having the same elastic properties in all directions.

JOIST.   A timber, steel, or reinforced concrete beam used in building.

KEYSTONE.   The stone at the crown of a masonry arch.

LIMIT STATES ANALYSIS.   A comprehensive series of analyses to determine stress, deflection (including vibration), cracking, and durability, and the margin of safety against collapse, under the service loads, in a structure being designed.

LINEAR ARCH.   An arch the shape of whose axis is such that the compressive stress across any cross-section due to the loads on it, including its own weight, is uniform.

LINTEL.   A beam spanning over a short opening.

LIVE LOAD.   Load due to vehicles, people, furniture, wind, etc., which is not permanently acting on a structure, as opposed to *dead load*.

LOAD-BEARING WALL CONSTRUCTION.   A system of multi-storey building in which the vertical and lateral loads are carried by vertical walls aligned in the same position in plan in all storeys, instead of by a skeleton frame.

LOAD FACTOR OF SAFETY (or LOAD FACTOR).   The ratio between the load to cause failure and the *service* or *working load*.

MECHANISM.   The condition of a structure when the ultimate strength has been reached at a sufficient number of points to render it unstable.

MEMBRANE.   A thin, flexible, sheet-like structural element acting entirely in tension and free from bending.

MEMBRANE FORCE.   The force in a membrane; also the compressive force in a thin shell which acts in the same way as a membrane but in compression.

MODULUS OF ELASTICITY.   A measure of elastic deformation, defined as the stress required to produce a unit strain.

MOMENT OF A FORCE (about a point or axis).   The product of the force and the shortest distance between the line of action of the force and the point or axis.

MOMENT OF RESISTANCE.   The capacity, or the ultimate capacity of a beam to resist bending.

MULLION.   A vertical bar sub-dividing a window opening.

NATURAL FREQUENCY.   The number of cycles of free oscillation of a structure or structural element in unit time (usually one second).

NATURAL PERIOD OF VIBRATION.   The time taken to complete one cycle of free oscillation; hence the reciprocal of the natural frequency.

NAVE.   The main body of a longitudinally planned church or cathedral.

NEUTRAL AXIS (or PLANE). The line (or plane) in a structural element at which the bending stresses change from tensile to compressive.

NEWTON (N).   The unit of force in the Standard International metric system. One newton is the force which when applied to a mass of one kilogram, produces an acceleration of 1 metre per second. One newton = 0.225 pounds weight.

ORTHOGONAL.   Intersecting at right angles.

PARABOLA.   The shape assumed by a weightless cable carrying a distributed vertical load whose intensity is uniform per unit of the horizontal span; also the path traced by a projectile as it falls under the action of gravity, if air resistance is neglected.

PILE.   A post or strut of timber, steel or reinforced or prestressed concrete driven into the ground, which enables load from a structure to be carried down to a depth where it can be safely borne by the ground.

PINNED JOINT.   A joint between two structural elements enabling them to rotate freely relative to each other.

PLASTIC COLLAPSE.   Failure of a structure by the development of enough plastic hinges to render part or all of it unstable.

PLASTIC DEFORMATION. Continued deformation under a constant or nearly constant load close to the ultimate strength, or when a plastic state has been reached over the whole of a section; in mild steel, when all the material at a section is undergoing deformation at the yield point and is on the horizontal portion of the stress-strain curve of Fig. 2.2.

PLASTIC HINGE. A section of a beam at which the bending moment is equal to the plastic moment, and at which, in consequence, an indefinite amount of relative rotation of the portions of the beam on either side occurs at constant bending moment.

PLASTIC MOMENT. Of a beam, its moment of resistance at a section when the stress everywhere at the section is undergoing plastic deformation in tension or compression.

PLATE-BANDE. A flat arch used especially in masonry construction.

POISSON'S RATIO (μ). In a piece of material under uniaxial stress, the ratio of the strain at right angles to the direction of stress to the strain in the direction of stress.

PRESTRESS. To apply loads to a structure or structural element for the purpose of modifying beneficially, and on a permanent basis, the state of internal stress.

PRESTRESSED CONCRETE. Concrete which is precompressed, usually by strands or rods of high tensile steel, in the zones in which tensile stresses occur under load.

PRINCIPAL STRESS. The maximum or minimum *direct* stress, either tensile or compressive, at any point within a structural element. In two-dimensional situations (as in membranes or thin webs) there are two principal stresses; in three-dimensional situations, three. Principal stresses are invariably at right angles to each other. One or two of them may, however, be zero.

PURLIN. A horizontal beam spanning between the principal rafters in a roof to carry the roof covering.

RAFTER. An inclined member in a roof truss extending from the ridge to the supporting wall.

REACTION. Force exerted by a support or another structural element in opposition to the loads.

REDUNDANT. A member or reaction whose introduction into a structure makes it statically indeterminate.

RESONANCE. A state in which a periodically varying disturbance reinforces the natural oscillations of a structure and thereby creates an amplitude considerably greater than would otherwise be the case.

RESULTANT. Of a set of forces, the single force which is equivalent to them in effect.

RIB. A linear projection from the surface of a structural element such as a shell; in arches, the term is applied to individual arched members.

RIGID FRAME. A frame in which some or all of the joints are rigid, making it statically indeterminate.

RIGID JOINT. A joint between structural members which does not allow any relative rotation to take place between them.

RING BEAM. See TENSION RING.

RISE. The height of the crown of an arch above the springings.

SECTION. A rolled or extruded form of iron, steel or other metal with a particular constant type of cross-section (e.g. I, L, or T).

SELF-WEIGHT. The weight of the structure itself.

SERVICE LOAD. The dead load of a structure, together with the live load which it is expected to carry when in service; this is also called the working load. The *ultimate load* is obtained by multiplying the various service loads by the appropriate load factor in each case.

SHEAR.   A type of racking or sliding deformation, and the structural action which gives rise to it (see Fig. 6.3).

SHEAR LAG.   Variations in the direct stresses in the flanges of a beam from the stresses calculated by simple bending theory, and developed as a result of shear deformations in the flanges.

SHEAR WALL.   A wall in a building designed to resist horizontal forces due to wind, earthquakes, or other causes by shear stresses in its own plane.

SHELL.   A thin singly or doubly curved structural element spanning a horizontal gap and capable of supporting loads mainly by direct compression or a combination of direct compression and tension.

SIMPLY SUPPORTED.   Of a beam, supported in such a manner that it is free to rotate at the supports and also to expand or contract longitudinally at one end.

SKELETON FRAME.   A frame which supports the walls, floors, roof, and the live load of a building, in the same way as a skeleton.

SLAB.   A structural element capable of spanning a horizontal gap, like a beam, but extended laterally to cover an area.

SPAN.   The distance between the supports of a structure.

SPECIFIC MODULUS (M).   The modulus of elasticity of a material divided by its weight per unit volume. Also a comparative measure of the stiffness of structures of given form but of different materials under the action of their own weight. (See Chapter 2.)

SPECIFIC STRENGTH (S).   The ultimate strength of a material divided by its weight per unit volume. Also the maximum length attainable by a bar of a material of uniform cross-section when hung from one end, before it breaks in tension under its own weight; similarly for a column in compression, with the proviso that it does not fail by buckling. It is a comparative measure of the size to which structures of a given form and different materials can be built before they fail under their own weight. (See Chapter 2.)

SPRINGING.   One of the points from which an arch or vault begins to curve upwards from its support.

STABLE EQUILIBRIUM.   A condition of a structural element or structure in which, if a slight disturbance is applied and then removed, the equilibrium is restored.

STABILITY.   A state of stable equilibrium.

STATICALLY DETERMINATE.   A structural situation in which all the forces or other actions are calculable by statics alone; also applied to particular structures.

STIFFENER.   A rib-like projection from a thin structural member, intended to increase its resistance to compressive forces.

STIFFNESS.   A measure of resistance of a structure or structural element to direct, bending, or other type of deformation; the force necessary to produce a given deformation.

STRAIN.   Deformation of a material per unit length.

STRENGTH.   The maximum load that a structure can carry before a specified limit of behaviour is reached.

STRESS.   Force per unit area.

STRESS FACTOR OF SAFETY.   The ratio between the stress at failure to the maximum permissible stress.

STRUCTURAL ELEMENT.   One of a series of basic units of construction, such as beams, struts, membrane, etc., from which structures are formed.

STRUCTURE.   A system of structural elements designed to support loads.

STRUT.   A structural element designed to resist compressive forces and usually forming part of a framed structure.

TENSION RING.   A circular structural element intended to resist the outward thrust of a dome.

TIE.   A slender structural element intended to resist tensile forces.

THRUST.   A compressive structural action or reaction.

THRUST LINE.   The line of action of the resultant compressive force in an arched structure.

TORSION.   Twisting action.

TRIANGLE OF FORCES.   A geometrical construction in which two forces are represented by two sides of a triangle; their resultant is then represented by the third side.

TRIAXIAL STRESS.   A stress condition at a point in a structure in which all three principal stresses are present.

TRUSS.   An assembly of ties and struts intended to act in a general manner as a beam.

UNSTABLE EQUILIBRIUM.   A condition of a structural element or structure in which, if a slight disturbance is applied, the equilibrium is destroyed and it collapses.

ULTIMATE STRENGTH.   Of a structure, the maximum load it can carry; of a material, the maximum stress.

VAULT.   A curved structural element, normally in the shape of part of a hollow cylinder, covering a horizontal area and supporting loads mainly in compression, by arch action.

VORTEX.   An eddy or local spiral motion in a stream of air.

VOUSSOIR.   A wedge-shaped block of masonry forming part of an arch.

WEB.   The plate or plates, normally vertical, connecting the flanges of a beam, and intended to resist mainly the shear force at any section.

WORKING LOAD.   See SERVICE LOAD.

WORKING STRESS.   The maximum permissible stress for working or service conditions.

YIELD STRESS.   The stress at which substantial plastic deformation starts.

YOUNG'S MODULUS.   The modulus of elasticity in direct tension or compression.

Further Reading

General

DA VINCI, LEONARDO (1952) *Notebooks, Selections from*, O.U.P., London.
GALILEO, G. (no date) *Dialogues Concerning Two New Sciences*, Dover, N.Y.
GORDON, J. E. (1968) *The New Science of Strong Materials*, Penguin Books, London.
MAINSTONE, R. (1975) *Developments in Structural Form*, Allen Lane, London.
NERVI, P. L. (1957) *The Works of Pier Luigi Nervi*, Architectural Press, London.
SALVADORI, M. and HELLER, R. (1963) *Structure in Architecture*, Prentice Hall, N.J.
THOMPSON, D'A. W. (1942) *On Growth and Form*, Cambridge U.P.
TORROJA, E. (1958) *The Philosophy of Structures*, California U.P.
TORROJA, E. (1958) *The Structures of Eduardo Torroja*, F. W. Dodge Corporation, N.Y.

Historical

HOPKINS, H. J. (1970) *A Span of Bridges*, David and Charles, Newton Abbot.
PANNELL, J. M. (1964) *An Illustrated History of Civil Engineering*, Thames & Hudson, London.
PARSONS, W. B. (1968) *Engineers and Engineering in the Renaissance*, M.I.T. Press, Cambridge, Mass.
ROLT, L.T.C. (1957) *Isambard Kingdom Brunel*, Longmans, London.
ROLT, L.T.C. (1958) *Thomas Telford*, Longmans, London.
ROLT, L.T.C. (1960) *George & Robert Stephenson*, Longmans, London.

Additional References

Chapter 2
DAVEY, N. (1961) *A History of Building Materials*, Phoenix, London.

Chapter 4
TIMOSHENKO, S. (1953) *History of Strength of Materials*, McGraw-Hill, N.Y.

Chapter 5
HEYMAN, J. (1966) The Stone Skeleton, *Int. J. of Solids & Structures*, 2, 249.

Chapter 8
SAMUELY, F. J. and WARD, P. J. A. (1952) *The Skylon*, Proc. Inst. Civ. Engrs., 1, 444.

Chapter 9
WILDER, THORNTON (1967) *The Bridge of San Luis Rey*. Harper-Row, N.Y.

Chapter 11
ARUP, O. (1969) The World of the Structural Engineer, *Structural Engineer*, 47, 3.
CREASY, L. R. (1959) Economics of Framed Structures, *Proc. Inst. C.E.*, 12, 237.

CROUCH, A. G. D. (1974) Bridge Aesthetics—a Sociological Approach, *Inst. Eng. Australia, Civil Engineering Transactions.*

Report of Committee of Inquiry into the Basis of Design and Method of Erection of Steel Box Girder Bridges, H.M.S.O., London (1973).

PUGSLEY, Sir Alfred (1966) *The Safety of Structures*, Arnold, London.

LEONHARDT, F. (1976) Looking Back on 45 Years as a Structural Engineer, *Structural Engineer*, **54**, 451.

Chapter 12

Report of Court of Inquiry upon the Circumstances attending the Fall of a Portion of the Tay Bridge (1880).

Report of Royal Commission . . . Quebec Bridge Inquiry—Sessional Papers 154 (Ottawa 1908).

AMMANN, O. H., KARMAN, T. VON and WOODRUFF, G. B. (1941) *The Failure of the Tacoma Narrows Bridge*, Pasadena, Cal.

Report of the Royal Commission into the Failure of King's Bridge, Government Printer, Melbourne (1963).

Report of the Inquiry into the Collapse of Flats at Ronan Point, Canning Town, H.M.S.O., London (1968).

Report of Royal Commission into the Failure of Westgate Bridge, Government Printer, Melbourne (1971).

SHUTE, NEVIL (1951) *No Highway*, Heinemann, London.

WALKER, A. and SIBLY, P. (12 Feb. 1976) When will an Oil Platform Fail? *New Scientist*.

WALKER, G. R. (1974) *Report on Cyclone Tracy—Effect on Buildings*, Melbourne.

Index